KU-422-646

DEAR GWENNIE, and JOAN, and PHYLLIS, and HUGH, and GEOFFREY, and URSULA, and GORDON, and BETTY, and ROSSITER, and others of the CROYDON JUNIOR LIBRARY PLAYERS too numerous to mention,

This book is yours.

All that it contains and describes was contrived for you, so the Dedication must also be yours whose vivid acting filled these little plays with a vital and moving charm.

Did you enjoy our brief collaboration as much as I did? I wonder! . . .

Well, here's the book—take it, and with it, my warm regards.

Good luck to you all!

> Your friend,
>
> CONELLY RICHARDS.

CROYDON: 1931.

TWO PLAYS

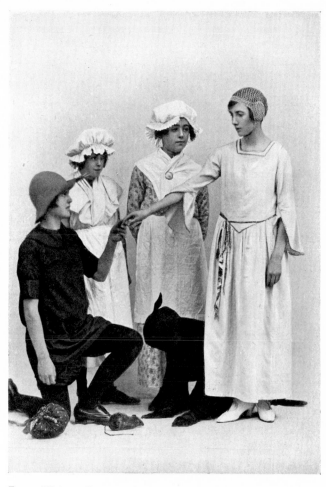

DICK: Mistress, I cannot find words with which to thank you—
but I will serve you to the end of my days!

TWO PLAYS

BY
CONELLY RICHARDS

★

DESIGNED TO BE ACTED
FOR THE MOST PART BY
YOUNG PLAYERS
WITHOUT SCENERY UPON
A
CURTAINED STAGE

★

ILLUSTRATED

COUNTY COUNCIL OF STIRLING
COUNTY LIBRARY
EDUCATION COMMITTEE

STIRLING
DISTRICT
LIBRARY

LONDON
AND TORONTO
J. M. DENT AND SONS LTD.

822
RIC

PRINTED IN GREAT BRITAIN AT
THE TEMPLE PRESS, LETCHWORTH, HERTS
FIRST PUBLISHED IN 1931

COPYRIGHT: PHILIP LEWIS EDMONDS, 1931

All rights reserved.

M 13695

These plays may be performed without payment of fees:
  (a) Where no charge, direct or indirect, is made for admission to the performance.
  (b) Where no collection is taken.
In all other cases application for permission to perform the plays must be addressed to: in the British Empire (except Canada): The Incorporated Society of Authors, Playwrights, and Composers, 11 Gower Street, London, W.C.1. In Canada and America: The Baker International Play Bureau, 41 Winter Street, Boston, Mass., U.S.A. The fee—to be paid in advance—for each and every representation of either play in the British Empire (except Canada) is ten shillings and sixpence; in Canada and America, two and a half dollars.

CONTENTS

LIST OF ILLUSTRATIONS

The studio-photographs are the work of *Lewis, George Street, Croydon.* The flashlight studies* of the actual production of *Ali Baba* were made by *C. Friend-Smith, Norbury Crescent, S.W.* 16.

ix

SOME EXPLANATIONS

THESE plays were written in an attempt to supply a band of enthusiastic young players with the sort of play they wanted.

They had grown disgruntled with the material at their disposal. It was either "infantile," "soft," or "wishie-washie"; at least, so they said.

Vigorous, capable actors of fourteen, resented being cast for "buttercups," and "daisies," and expected to speak in rhymed couplets; and keen intelligence revolted from pretty inanities wherein "kitchenmaids" spoke with the same characterless precision as "princesses" . . .

A few carefully chosen questions, and some attentive listening, elicited other salient points; girls and boys alike subscribing to them.

Contrary to expectation the young players did not object to taking part in fairy-tale plays, *provided* that the writing was "strong," and that the characters spoke "naturally." "Let a chap talk slang wherever a chap *would* talk slang!" we were told.

Neither did the actors want to sing or dance. They wanted to *act*; and to *keep on acting*. They demanded a play, so written and so produced, that it would go "right ahead" with nothing to interrupt it. "Keep to the rails," they said. "No mucking about, and wasting time!" . . .

Here was something to go upon! . . . So, after due deliberation, a play on the theme of *Dick Whittington* was constructed, read to the cast, and —to the trembling author's surprise and pleasure— accepted on the spot without one dissentient voice!

Never for a moment did the players appear to doubt the ultimate success of the show. And a real success they made of it, thanks to their hard preparatory work, and the vim with which they "put it over."

By general request *Ali Baba* followed *Dick*, and proved even more popular than his predecessor.

.   .   .   .   .

We had to perform our plays in a room in use all day as a library, and most evenings as a lecture-room. So there could be no question of elaborate or permanent stage fixtures.

This is how we tackled the problem:

The platform measured twenty feet in width, by eleven feet six inches in depth—round figures. On one side the platform was lined with bookshelves having a plain wall with picture rail above. On the other side there were more bookshelves, with a large window above. At the back of the platform was a screen on to which lantern-slides were projected. A door at one corner of the platform led, by way of a few steps, to a room beyond. This was the only available way on to, and off, the stage.

We commenced by stringing stranded wire to form a square bay, with splayed sides, leaving a passage-way behind. From this wire we hung six curtains of light buff casement cloth. These were left to form a plainly draped background, or else looped up to represent archways, and the like. (In the illustration to *Ali Baba*, page 70, can be seen an entrance contrived by clipping up the curtains with spring clothes-pegs).

Three feet "up stage" we hung the first, or "inner," draw-curtains. These when closed formed the background to our "front stage" scenes (see *Ali Baba*, page 84). They were dark green in colour.

At the very edge of the stage were the second draw-curtains; navy-blue, this time. These moved but twice in a performance; namely, at the beginning, and at the end. Between these two points only the "inner" curtains were used.

It will readily be seen how perfectly this arrangement enabled us to meet the demand for *rapid action*. The first four scenes of *Dick Whittington*—"full stage" scenes—had only very short waits between them; the remaining six scenes being played alternately "full stage," and then "front stage," without a break; as was the whole of *Ali Baba*. . . .

Now a word about lighting. In front of the stage and on wires stretched across the room from picture-rail to picture-rail, were hung four wooden, tin-lined flood-boxes. Four flood-boxes — made from biscuit tins—were used on the stage; two right and left behind the "inner" draw-curtains (the chief function of these being to throw different tints upon the buff curtains, and so enable us to

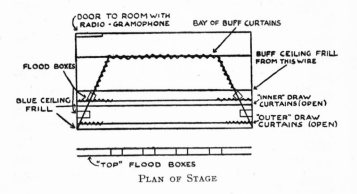

PLAN OF STAGE

change the apparent colour of the background), and two others, between the "inner" and "outer" draw-curtains.

The plan appended will, it is hoped, make all this clear.

To supply music when necessary, a radio-gramophone was installed in the room behind the stage, and connected with the two loud-speakers suspended in front of the "outer" draw-curtains. There was also another loud-speaker behind the scenes used to produce music and sounds "off." These speakers made it possible for us to reproduce *Bow Bells* with accuracy and realism. The fine Columbia Record, No. 4082, coming over with great effect. (The speakers, and the "top lights" can be seen in the illustration to *Ali Baba*, page 84).

.   .   .   .   .

The necessary properties and accessories should be made by the players themselves, and will be found to supply very fascinating amusement. Care must be taken that all designs are suitable, and well executed, and afterwards carried out with exactness, good finish, and attention to detail.

Only a little stage furniture, and very few heavy properties are needed, even for *Dick Whittington*; whilst *Ali Baba* only calls for a "divan." The use and arrangement of the "grass bank" in the former play is explained in the text. For the "kitchen scene" a white wood table, and one chair, will suffice. The "doorstep" in Scene III forms the "dais" in Scene V.

All "crowds" have been studiously avoided. We would have nothing to do with "courtiers dancing a gavotte," or the like. We didn't *want* to dance, and mobs and evolutions are impossible, or silly, on a small stage; moreover, they hold up the action and so blur the outline of the story. They are best suggested by "noises off." (See "Dick," Scene X).

DICK WHITTINGTON

AN EXTEMPORIZATION
ON A WELL-KNOWN THEME

To
" M "
who said
" Don't *talk* about it—
write it!"

THE PEOPLE

* FATHER TIME.

* FATHER CHRISTMAS.

* AN OLD WOMAN.

DICK WHITTINGTON (*a poor lad seeking his fortune*).

SMUT (*his cat*).

ALICE (*daughter of Alderman Fitzwarren of the City of London*).

ROSA ⎫
MARY ⎬ (*friends of Alice*).

ARABELLA (*cook to the Fitzwarrens*).

KITTY (*a kitchen maid*).

CAPTAIN WINDLASS (*Commander of the "Pretty Alice"*).

THE EMPEROR CHUNGERGUNC OF WOOZZOOLLOO.

HE HO HUM ⎫
HE HO HO ⎬ (*his bodyguard*).

* These characters should be played by adults. The "Old Woman" by someone small, and slight of build.

THE SCENES

SCENE I (FULL STAGE)

The Happy Isles of Ever After

TIME *is discovered asleep on a bank, snoring contentedly. . . . The sound of sleigh bells is heard, very faintly. . . . They come nearer, accompanied now by the trotting of hoofs. . . . Next the unseen vehicle is brought to a standstill with a great noise of stamping and jingling, and the voice of* FATHER CHRISTMAS *rings out as he speaks to his steeds.*

CHRISTMAS. [*Without.*] Whoa, there, my beauties! Whoa, my dandies! Whoa, there, boys; well done, well done! A splendid journey! . . . Rest, my darlings, rest! . . . And now to find my quarry!

[*He enters ; and sees* TIME.
Ah *there* he is! And a sight for the gods in very truth! Behold TIME marking time!
[*He grabs* TIME *by the forelock, and shakes it playfully.*
Wake up, Gaffer! . . . Wake up!

TIME. [*Waking confused.*] Eh . . . Eh . . . What? . . .

CHRISTMAS. [*Shaking him by the shoulder, and*

5

speaking with gentle raillery.] Wake up, I say!
. . . Don't you know what *hour* it is?

TIME. [*Looking dazed*.] Steady. . . . Steady. . . .
[*Helped by* CHRISTMAS *he rises to his feet in slow
stages*.] Easy does it, Nicholas, old friend! . . .
I'm not so young as I used to be. . . .

CHRISTMAS. No, Gaffer, indeed you are not! . . .
I suppose that is why you are always sneaking
off here—outside your radius—to take forty
winks among the Immortals. . . . Man created
you to be the proof and measure of Eternity,
and you reward him by growing older every year!

TIME. [*Testily*]. Well, well, you needn't rub it
in! . . . I know well enough that I shall die
some day—Man, who created me, will eventually
destroy me—and my twin brother Space into
the bargain—but when he does so he will destroy
himself at the same moment! Ah! ha! . . . We
shall not perish alone! . . .

[*After a thoughtful chuckle he continues briskly*.
But not *yet*! . . . Not *just* yet! . . . My days
on earth are not what they were—Man is doing
his best to wear me out—but there's life in the
old dog yet! . . . I'll give him a run for his
money before we all go up in a puff of smoke—
see if I don't . . . see if I don't. . . .

[*A dreamy look comes into his eyes*.
Just so long as I can slip out here to the Happy
Isles where the Beautiful Deathless live beyond—

CHRISTMAS. [*Who has been growing restless during*

this long speech, breaks in.] Tut, tut, Gaffer, you grow garrulous in your old age! My errand is urgent, and brooks of no delay. With all your talk you have not yet answered my question. . . . Do you know what hour it is?

TIME. Bless you, good Saint, how should I? . . . This is my Sanctuary. . . . Here, in the Happy Ever After, there are *no* hours. Glory be! Only Peace, Beauty, Holy Aspirations, Flowering Dreams, and the Sunshine of the Love of Little Children! . . .

CHRISTMAS. [*Stamping with vexation.*] Holy Smoke! He's at it again! . . . Have done, I say, with your high-falutin' and come down to plain brass tacks! . . . You mentioned Children just now (well for you you did, shows you're not altogether wool-gathering), well, it's on behalf of the Children that I am come. . . . If you were not so bemused with idleness you would have remembered ere this that on Earth the Twelfth Hour has struck: the Twelfth Hour of the Year! The Children's Hour! *My* Hour! . . . *Christmas!* . . .

TIME. [*"Coming to" with a jerk.*] God bless my soul—why—so it is!

CHRISTMAS. Ah! So you are awake at last, are you! . . . And high time too, I fancy! . . . What a good thing that you had me to "carry on" for you, wasn't it? . . . Oh, don't look so scared! I 've kept things going all right in the way of Good Will, Good Cheer, and the like, I

can tell you. I 've not overlooked many stockings
either, I flatter myself—but one insistent demand I
cannot meet: My Festival is not complete without
Stories, and these you, and you alone, can call
from. their Happy Rest. Here, in the Ever
After Isles, dwell all the Heroes and Heroines
of all the Stories ever told or dreamed of. Come!
Listen! . . . At this instant the Children of
—— are calling for a story—which of our dear
old friends will you send them? Yonder waits
my sleigh to bear your choice to Earth in the
twinkling of an eye—but the choice must be
yours! Quickly! . . . *Quickly!* . . .

TIME. [*Echoing the words in a tense undertone.*]
Quickly! . . . Quickly! . . . They all say that
to me now! . . . [*Then with a burst of fury.*]
But I *won't* be spurred! . . . I *won't!* . . . [*As
suddenly as it has blazed up, his anger dies down
again, and it is almost brokenly that he murmurs.*]
I am old, and you fluster me. . . . I *can't*
decide! . . . [*He takes a step or two, listless and
dejected—in a flash his eyes light up, and he cries
out.*] They shall choose among themselves! . . .
I will call some of them here, and *they* shall
decide! . . . [*He claps his hands and calls.*]
Aladdin! . . . Red-Riding Hood! . . . Dick
Whittington! . . . Babes in the Wood! . . .
Cinderella! . . . Ali Baba! . . .

  [*These, and others (at the discretion of the
      producer) run in to crowd about him in a*

*many-coloured group, pulling him this way
and that with shouts and laughter.*

Peace, I say! . . . Quiet! . . . Have done, you
rogues! . . . Peace! . . . Peace! Listen, my
Darlings, my Immortal Ones—the Children of
—— are calling for a story, and Christmas, here,
is waiting to take one of you post-haste to
Earth—which is it to be?

STORIES. [*All speaking together.*] I! . . . I! . . .
Take me! . . . Please! . . . Oh, please! . . .

CHRISTMAS. [*Interposing with a laugh.*] Here—
steady! . . . I can't take you *all* ! . . . I only
want *one*!

STORIES. [*Flinging themselves upon him.*] Take me!
. . . No, me! . . . Me! . . . Oh, please, me!

CHRISTMAS. [*Laughing, and playfully pushing them
from him.*] Silence! . . . Silence, I say! . . .
Time must choose. Now, Gaffer—quick!

TIME. [*Shaking with annoyance.*] I tell you I *can't*
decide! . . . I 'm all upset——

CHRISTMAS. Then I 'll bind your eyes, and you
must pick one at random!

TIME. Aha! Clever Nicholas! . . . Always a
bright boy! . . . Always a bright boy!

[CHRISTMAS *binds* TIME's *eyes with a handker-
chief, who thereupon lunges and clutches at
the running, dodging* STORIES *until, at the
ending of a huge semicircular sweep of the
arm, he seizes* CHRISTMAS, *who has not
retired very far apart after the blindfolding.*

Ah, now I 've caught someone! . . . Hold my
staff. . . . Hold my staff. . . .

> [*A* STORY *takes his scythe, and* TIME *carefully*
> *explores his captive with his hands. . . .*
> *When they reach the beard, he cries out.*

Why, it 's *Nicholas*! . . . Go away, you wicked
Saint—you 're not playing! . . . Go away! Go
away! . . .

> [*The* STORIES *are laughing delightedly as* TIME
> *thrusts* CHRISTMAS *from him.*

Now! . . . Again. . . . I 'll have one of you
in a minute!

> [*He takes back the scythe, and the game is renewed*
> *until finally he captures* DICK WHITTINGTON,
> *who cries:*

DICK. Hurrah! . . . Hurrah!!

> [*The other* STORIES *groan disappointedly.*

CHRISTMAS. [*Unbinding* TIME'S *eyes.*] So it 's to be
Dick, eh? . . . Well, Dick, will you come and
tell your Story to the Children of ——?

DICK. Aye, Father, right willingly! . . . And *act*
it, too—an' it please you!

CHRISTMAS. That 's a good lad! . . . Now; into
my sleigh without more ado.

> [*They all laughingly hustle* DICK *towards the*
> *sleigh. . . . He resists ; and makes as if*
> *to speak. At length, gaining a hearing, he*
> *cries:*

DICK. Stop! Stop! . . . All in good time! . . .
Pray how can I go without Smut? What would

the children say to Dick Whittington without his Cat?

ALL. Yes, the Cat! . . . Smut! . . . The Cat!

DICK. [*Calling.*] Puss! puss! Come along, Smut! Puss, puss!

> [*Loud mewings are heard, and* SMUT *capers in. Everybody makes a fuss of him.*

CHRISTMAS. In you go, both of you! . . . [*He turns to* TIME.] And you, too, Gaffer! There's work for you below—you're not dead yet, you know!

> [DICK, SMUT, *and* TIME *are hustled to the sleigh amid a hubbub of laughter and talk. . . . Soon sleigh bells, and trotting hoofs are heard, and the* STORIES *break into loud cheers, and cries of "Good-bye,* DICK!" *"Good-bye,* SMUT!" . . . *"Good-bye! . . . Good-bye!" as the curtains are closed.*

SCENE II (Full Stage)

On the Northern Heights above London

The bank used in the previous scene has been pushed to the other side and a milestone set up behind it.

Dick *and* Smut *enter by the auditorium, limping and weary.*

Dick. Come along, Smut. . . . Are you very tired? . . . Well, so is master, old man. Dreadfully, dreadfully tired! . . . Cheer up, Smut; we must keep up our spirits, you know! . . . Only a little farther—and then—*London!* And gold for the picking up! . . . Think of that, Smut! The old sailor down home said London was paved with gold. . . . Oh, Smut; it's worth being tired—even as tired as we are—to win riches, isn't it?

[Dick *has reached the stage by now, and is looking R, so does not perceive an* Old Woman *who has entered L. and stands watching and listening. . . .* Dick *puts his hand on the milestone before him, and at the same moment catches sight of London almost at his feet.*

Look! . . . Look! . . . *London!* Beautiful, glorious London! . . . More beautiful than ever I dreamed, and, just down there in the valley;

12

near, Smut, very near! . . . How lovely it looks
—see how it gleams in the sunlight! That must
be the gold, Smut! . . . I don't feel tired now—
I could *run* the distance! [*But weariness over-
comes him again, and he sinks heavily on to the
bank.*] All the same, I think we *had* better rest
a little—so as to look our freshest when we reach
the City. . . .

[*The* OLD WOMAN *slowly advances.*

OLD WOMAN. Can you spare a trifle for a poor
lone woman, young master?

[*Taken by surprise* DICK *starts, looks round,
rises, and then fumbles in his little leather
pouch.*

DICK. A groat is all I have in the wide world, good
mother, but to that you are welcome.

[*He holds it out to her.*

OLD WOMAN. [*Drawing back.*] Nay, lad! Poor as
I am, I cannot take your all!

DICK. [*Again pressing the money on her.*] Take it,
I pray you, for I shall soon have riches, and to
spare! . . . Yonder lies London, whither I am
bound, and there gold is to be had for the picking
up. Why, I am told the very streets are paved
with it! . . . Take my groat, it is yours gladly
—I would it were more!

[*The* OLD WOMAN *appears touched by his
smiling sincerity. She gazes intently at
him for a brief space—then seats herself
on the bank.*

OLD WOMAN. Lad—have you a mother?

> [DICK'S *smile fades, and he shakes his head sadly.*

DICK. Nay, good woman. . . . She has been dead these twelve months.

> [*He drops upon the bank beside the* OLD WOMAN, *who lays her hand upon his knee. . . . After a pause he continues.*

I have been miserable without her—happiness and kindliness forsook our home when she left us—so [*Shaking his depression from him.*] I am come to London to seek my fortune—along with Smut, here!

> [*While* DICK *has been speaking the bells have begun to ring very softly and are gradually growing louder. . . .* DICK *does not notice them, but the* OLD WOMAN *listens with growing wonder.*

OLD WOMAN. What is your name, lad?

DICK. Richard Whittington, ma'am; but I am usually called Dick.

OLD WOMAN. [*With growing excitement.*] Then 'tis to you the bells are speaking!

DICK. The bells?

OLD WOMAN. Aye—the bells.

DICK. To *me*?

OLD WOMAN. Aye, lad; to you—don't you hear them?

DICK. I hear bells—but naught else!

> [*Both listen again, intently.*

OLD WOMAN. Let me see your hand!

[DICK *holds out his right hand.*
No, the other. . . .

[DICK *obeys, and she gazes at the palm.*
Aye—so the bells speak true!

DICK. [*Puzzled and intrigued.*] What say the bells?
. . . What mean you? . . . You are riddling and
fortune-telling in one! . . . What see you in my
hand?

OLD WOMAN. [*Again examining the hand.*] I see a
coach—a grand coach—and *you* within it. . . .
Three times you pass, bowing left and right, as
a multitude acclaims you. . . . And by your side,
proudly sharing your honours, sits one prized
above all riches, and dearer to you than life
itself.

[*While the* OLD WOMAN *has been speaking the
bells have died away into silence.*

DICK. [*Laughing and bewildered.*] In sooth, a goodly
fortune, good dame! . . . But the bells—what
is their message?

OLD WOMAN. That I may not say, for the time is
not yet ripe. . . . They will speak to you
again—in the Hour of Tribulation you will hear
their voices—see to it that you mark them well!

DICK. [*Still more puzzled, and pulling a wry face.*]
"Tribulation," say you! Anon you spoke of
wealth and honours—I like not your *second*
prophecy!

OLD WOMAN. Lad—all fruits worth the winning

are the reward of suffering. You will succeed—
but you will suffer. . . .
See, take this tiny bean. [*She takes it from under
her cloak.*] Wear it ever above your heart and
do not part with it till Love impels. When
trouble presses, lay your hand upon it, and be
of good cheer.

> [*She places the bean, which is strung upon a
> ribbon, about* DICK's *neck.*

DICK. Thank you, good mother!

> [*The* OLD WOMAN *rises, and moves away.*

But stay—tell me more!

OLD WOMAN. [*Looking back.*] I cannot! . . . My
task is accomplished! . . . Listen for the message
of the bells. . . . Good luck go with you. . . .
And remember me when your ship comes home !

> [*She passes out.*

DICK. [*Making to hurry after the* OLD WOMAN.]
Stay! . . . Stay! . . . [*He stares in astonishment, and then rubs his eyes as if doubting their
evidence.*] Why, she is gone! . . . She walked
but three paces along the road—and now, is
vanished! . . . It is as if I had dreamed her!
. . . [*He feels about his throat.*] Yet I have the
bean—that is real enough. And I can remember
every word of that wonderful prophecy. . . .
Oh, to realize it! . . . Come, Smut, old man—
to London—and Fortune!

THE CURTAINS CLOSE

SCENE III (Full Stage)

Outside the Rear of Alderman Fitzwarren's House in the City.

It is morning. . . . Dick, *homeless and well-nigh starving, is discovered asleep on the Alderman's back doorstep, his head pillowed on his bundle, and* Smut *curled up beside him.*

Enter Alice Fitzwarren, *the Alderman's daughter, with two girl friends,* Rosa *and* Mary. *They are half laughing, half fearful, having evidently been about some untoward doings.*

ALICE. There—'tis over! . . . Now we have but to regain our homes unchallenged, and all is well!

MARY. Easier said than done!

ROSA. Why, Mary?

MARY. *Why?* . . . Are we not already later than we planned? Our households will be astir. It is full certain that we cannot now enter undetected. . . . [*She pouts.*] I doubt not that we were foolish and unwise to risk a rating—and all for vanity!

ALICE. [*Half laughing; half scolding.*] Vanity forsooth; for shame, Mary! Are you turning your coat? Once you were keenest of us all on the escapade — as well you know — and now you talk like Madame Prudence, all propriety and properness!

[MARY *would reply, but is interrupted by* ROSA.

ROSA. If it be true that we are late, why are we tarrying? . . . We can at least *try* to escape a rating. . . . Yet in truth I would consider one small fee for all this morn hath given us! . . . Oh, Alice, is not the dawn fair? The Earth re-born from morning mists — the lark's song falling like silver rain from Heaven—and the cool dew like fairy kisses upon one's face! . . .

ALICE. Ah, and to think of all the maidens in this Great City, we three, alone, have done homage to Spring by dabbling in the dew this May morning.

MARY. Then let us hope we get our reward! And not just a scolding—or a horrid, unbecoming cold—or *both*!

ROSA. Mary!

ALICE. [*Pretending to shake* MARY.] You faithless little wretch! . . . And now—home without more ado! I shall enter by the kitchen, for Kitty the kitchenmaid is first abroad, and she, good little soul, will not betray me. Quickly— for time flies!

[*They embrace, and part.* . . . ALICE *stands for a moment or two looking after the others and waving her hand. Next she turns to run into the house, almost tripping over* DICK

as she does so. She draws back with a
smothered "Oh!"—then approaches gingerly,
bending over him, and scanning his face and
figure with a curiosity which merges into
something very like approval.

Poor boy! . . .

    [*Very gently she stoops and almost tenderly she*
brushes the hair from his forehead that she
may the better see his face. But gentle as
is her touch, DICK *wakes, shrinking back*
as one in expectation of a blow.

DICK. Don't — I'm doing no harm! . . . [*He*
scrambles to his feet.] I'll go—I was sleeping,
that's all.

ALICE. So I see. . . . But why do you sleep on
my father's doorstep?

DICK. Because I have nowhere else to go! . . . For
days have I tramped this stony city, a butt for
kicks and cuffs, and vile words; at last, weary
and sick at heart, I fell asleep yonder. . . . I
am sorry if I have offended, and will go at once.

                        [*He turns away.*

ALICE. Stay! . . . How came you in this plight?
Have you *no* home?

DICK. None since my mother died. . . . After
that I grew unhappy, and being led to believe
that London was paved with gold, came hither
to seek my fortune.

                [*He bursts out with sudden fury.*

Gold! . . . Gold!! There is no gold here! None!

. . . Only darkness — squalor — mud — filth — cruelty—and venom! . . . Why, I cannot even get the humblest work, or the wherewithal to buy myself a crust of bread, or a sup of milk for Smut, here! . . .Gold, forsooth! ! !

ALICE. Poor boy! . . . Poor little cat! . . .

> [*She fondles* SMUT, *her eyes the while on* DICK. *Impulsively she draws near to him, asking with a smile:*

You love the country?

DICK. [*Wistfully.*] Already I am homesick for the woods and fields!

ALICE. [*Confidentially.*] I, too, love these things, though I am city-born. And this morning— with Rosa and Mary—I have been, in secret, to the nearer fields—it being May Day—to bathe my face in the dew o' the dawn!

DICK. [*Smiling.*] That is what the milkmaids do at home—'tis said they owe their "cream and roses" to it!

> [*For the first time he looks squarely at* ALICE *and his eyes are held. . . . It is a long, long look, before he says:*

But such practices are not for *you*——

> [*He pulls himself up abruptly. . . . There is a pause. . . . Then* SMUT *ambles forward and places the body of a rat between them, patting and playing with it. The tension is broken. . . .* ALICE *steps back with a little scream.*

Have no fear—it is dead.

[*He stoops, picks up the body by the tail, holding it out for* ALICE'S *reassurance, whilst* SMUT *paws at it, mewing.*

Good cat! . . . Clever pussy! . . .

[*He restores the body to* SMUT *and fondles him.*

ALICE. Is he skilled in catching such vermin?

DICK. Aye, in truth! He should be called "Nimrod"—not Smut!

ALICE. [*Briskly; with the air of one who sees her course plain.*] Then my father hath need of him! . . . What is your name?

DICK. Dick Whittington.

ALICE. Straightway will I petition my father for you both. Dick Whittington and his Cat shall beg their bread no more! Father will not refuse me, never fear! . . . Stay here—I command you—till I return.

[ALICE *turns to enter the house.* . . . SMUT *has returned to the step, where he lies gently dabbing at the body of the dead rat. Before* ALICE *can reach the door,* ARABELLA, *the cook, makes to come out, half trips over* SMUT, *staggers, almost falling, until* DICK *and* ALICE *succeed in steadying her.* . . . *This commotion has excited* SMUT, *and he capers about.* ARABELLA, *catching sight of him fully for the first time, screams aloud and runs across the stage. As she does so, her apron strings blow out behind, to the delight*

> *of* SMUT, *who pursues them joyously. . . .*
> *Both race round, circus-wise, several times,*
> *to the accompaniment of shrieks from*
> ARABELLA *and helpless laughter from* DICK
> *and* ALICE. *. . . At length* ARABELLA *flings*
> *her arms round* DICK'S *neck, crying:*

ARABELLA. Save me! . . . Help! . . . Save me! . . .

DICK. Fear not, good woman!

ARABELLA. [*Suddenly thrusting* DICK *from her.*] Fellow! I am no man's "good woman."

ALICE. Smut will not hurt you, Cook, dear!

ARABELLA. Neither, Miss Alice, am I your "dear Cook!" . . . Shame on you to laugh at my misfortunes! Shame on you to plot my confusion with a beggar, and a wild beast!

> [*She throws her apron over her head, and sobs*
> *violently.*

ALICE. Nay, Arabella, we have not conspired against you—and Smut, here, is no wild beast, but a great catcher of rats and mice. As for Dick Whittington, he is no beggar, and I am about to intercede with my father on his behalf.

ARABELLA. Sakes alive, child! Are you mad or bewitched! . . . Intercede with the good Alderman for yon dirty fellow and his ravening monster! I can scarcely contain my feeling! . . . Had I not a sweet temper, and a honeyed tongue, I could——

ALICE. [*Imperiously.*] No more! Peace, I say—
and that, quickly! . . . [*She continues with quiet
dignity.*] Good Arabella, you forget yourself.
Since my lady mother was laid to rest, I have
been mistress here, and on this matter I have
spoken. . . . [*She turns to* DICK.
Master Whittington, I pray you stir not before
I return.

[ALICE *passes into the house.* . . . DICK *and*
ARABELLA *stand gazing after her.* . . .
Suddenly, and without warning, ARABELLA
turns upon DICK *like a veritable whirlwind.*

ARABELLA. And now, you good-for-nothing knave
—you violent vagabond—get you gone! ! ! Oh,
that a worthless beggar should sow discord
between me and my sweet mistress! . . . Get
you gone, I say!—ere I beat you, or call for the
Watch! !

DICK. [*Quietly standing his ground.*] Mistress Alice
bade me await her return, I cannot go till she
release me.

[ARABELLA *steps forward as if to strike* DICK,
and in so doing steps on SMUT'S *paw. He
sets up a yowl, and spits at her.*

ARABELLA. [*Retreating to the doorstep in a panic.*]
Call him off! . . . Help! . . . He's going to fly
at me! . . . Shoo!—shoo!!

DICK. [*With a smile.*] He'll not hurt you—will
you, Smut?

ARABELLA. [*Covering her retreat with as much*

dignity as she can muster.] Ho, indeed! . . .
Well, I 'll not stay here to be insulted and eaten
alive!

> [*She drops her voice and speaks with almost*
> *malignant intensity.*

But look you here—if you thrust yourself, and
that wild beast, into this house, you 'll regret it,
I promise you, as sure as my name 's Arabella
Wagglechin!

> [*At this point* SMUT, *who has been crouching as*
> *if about to spring, leaps playfully into the*
> *the air, causing* ARABELLA *to rush into the*
> *house with a wild yell.* DICK, *left alone,*
> *brushes down his clothes, and in straightening*
> *his tunic he feels the bean beneath it. . . .*
> *He draws out the talisman by its ribbon, and*
> *gazes at it reflectively.*

DICK. Strange! . . . Many times of late have I
been on the point of flinging this from me, and
cursing the Old Woman and her mocking
prophecy; but something ever held me back. . . .
Last night, when I seemed at the end of my
tether, I lay down with my hand upon this gift;
and when I awoke, it was to see Miss Alice bending
over me, and to hear the first kind words that
London has brought me.

> [*A sound as of someone approaching causes him*
> *to thrust the bean back into his bosom. . . .*
> ALICE *returns from the house, followed by*
> ARABELLA *and the kitchen-maid* KITTY.

ALICE. Dick Whittington, my father, Alderman
Fitzwarren, bids you to serve him as page. . . .
Bring Smut and come within, for he would speak
to you forthwith.

[DICK *drops on one knee and kisses her hand.*

DICK. Mistress, I cannot find words with which to
thank you—but I will serve you to the end of
my days!

[*He rises and stands stiffly.*

ARABELLA. Lack-a-me! Do I hear aright? . . .
This vagabond and his monster to be taken into
the house! We shall all be murdered in our beds!

ALICE. Cook, be silent! . . . Dick is to have good
lodging. Mark that well.

[ALICE *enters the house followed by* DICK *and*
SMUT.

ARABELLA. [*Almost beside herself.*] Good lodging!
. . . Good lodging! . . . Oh, yes! He shall
have the attic above the stable, and if he be not
eaten by rats in a week, cat or no cat, then
Satan himself must be his protector! . . .
[*Then with an immense effort of self-control.*] Had
I not the tongue and temper of a thousand
cherubs I could say more. . . . But [*Exploding
again.*], but, mark my words—*even a worm will
turn!*

KITTY. [*Meekly.*] Yes, Cook—but when it does it
is still a worm.

ARABELLA. [*Grabbing* KITTY *and shaking her.*]
Out upon you, you worthless baggage! Out

upon you! . . . [*She thrusts the girl roughly into the house; and standing upon the doorstep declaims.*] Alack the day! Spurned! Insulted! All have turned upon me! . . . Oh, that I should have lived to herd with murderers and monsters!!

[*She enters the house as the curtains close.*

SCENE IV (Full Stage)

The Kitchen at Alderman Fitzwarren's

KITTY *is discovered dusting the table. . . .* DICK
enters, neatly dressed as a page. KITTY *looks
up at him with evident admiration.*

DICK. Say, Kitty—what's afoot? . . . Captain
Windlass has been shut up with the master
for nigh upon an hour.

KITTY. Lor, now, ain't you 'eard? . . . Master be
agoin' to send 'is great ship, the *Pretty Alice*, for
the biggest voyage as ever was! Right round
the 'ole world, a-tradin' with all them heathums,
and canibiles, and the like. . . . An' wot's
more, we're all to have a finger in the pie—as
yer might say!

DICK. We? . . . A finger in the pie? . . . But
how, Kitty?

KITTY. I'll tell yer! . . . Captain Windlass be
a-comin' round soon to collect anything we like
to give 'im—it must be something of our very
own, o' course—to trade on the voyage.

DICK. To trade on the voyage?

KITTY. Yes! . . . Don't yer see? Some o' these
poor naked, savage heathums ain't got none of
the things as we 'ave, and time and again they'll

give a mort o' gold for something as ain't worth a groat here in London. . . . It's a great chance, don't yer see, and one as all can share!

DICK. [*Musingly.*] A great chance. . . . Would that *I* had something to send! . . . Oh, Kitty, if only I could make my fortune! I don't want to sound ungrateful—you've all been so kind to me in the year that I have spent here—if only Arabella were not so set against poor Smut there had been no shadow upon it— for myself I care not for her nagging tongue— but I want to rise, to take a better place in the world, to——

KITTY. [*Sniffing.*] Yes—and I know for why!

> [DICK *looks up questioningly.*

[*With much emphasis.*] MISS ALICE!

DICK. [*Alarmed and confused.*] Kitty! Hush! You mustn't say such things!

KITTY. [*Tossing her head.*] Ho, no! Of course not! . . . [*Comes close to* DICK *and speaks in a low, meaning tone.*] Thinks of 'er all day, and dreams of 'er all night, don't yer?——

DICK. Be silent!

KITTY. [*Continuing.*] Yes, and never so much as a thought for those nearer to you in station wot 'ave stood yer friend time and agin! [*She weeps.*

DICK. [*Looking contrite.*] Look here—Kitty——

> [CAPTAIN WINDLASS *is heard without, shouting "Yo, ho, me hearties!" He enters.*

CAPTAIN. Yo, ho! Belay there! . . . I'm collectin'

for the voyage. What be ye a-sending from the kitchen, may I ask?

[ARABELLA *enters, all smiles and smirks at the sight of the* CAPTAIN.

ARABELLA. Lawks, Captain—'andsomer than ever, I do declare!

CAPTAIN. That ain't never you, Mrs. Wagglechin, be it? . . . Why, shiver my timbers if you don't grow more like yer own daughter every day o' yer life! . . . An' what be *you* a-goin' to send to foreign parts abroad?

[SMUT *enters.* . . . ARABELLA, *in reply to the* CAPTAIN, *holds up a pair of red stockings, one in each hand, beaming more expansively than before.*

ARABELLA. These! . . . Ain't they lovely?

[*She dangles the stockings before the* CAPTAIN'S *eyes.* SMUT, *taking this to be an invitation to play, springs forward, patting at them with his paws. In a moment* ARABELLA *forgets her smiles, and with a yell of fury makes for* SMUT.

Leave them be, you horrid beast! Get out! Shoo! Shoo!

[*Round and round she chases* SMUT *till he suddenly slips out leaving her baffled and panting.*

Wait till I catch that limb of Satan, that's all! Just wait!

DICK. For shame, Cook! Why are you so hard on

poor Smut? He's a good cat, and has almost
rid your kitchen of rats and mice, and yet you
have nothing for him but abuse and cruelty!
It would break my heart to part with Smut, yet
if I could find him a really good home I would
willingly send him away that he might escape
your tongue and temper!

[*By now* ARABELLA *is almost beside herself.*

ARABELLA. Temper! . . . TEMPER!!

[*The* CAPTAIN, *evidently struck by something
in* DICK'S *outburst, stems the tide of*
ARABELLA'S *impending eloquence.*

CAPTAIN. Your pardon, ma'am! . . . Now, Dick,
me young shaver—what be *you* a-goin' to send
on this 'ere voyage?

DICK. Nothing, Captain—for I have nothing to
send.

[ALICE *enters at the back and stands listening.*

CAPTAIN. [*In a significant tone.*] Are you *quite
sure* o' that?

DICK. Yes—quite sure.

CAPTAIN. [*Looking at him meaningly.*] What about
the cat?

DICK. Smut?

CAPTAIN. Yes, Smut! . . . See here, lad—you said
just now as if you knew of a good 'ome fer the
cat you'd send 'im straight along. . . . Well,
the *Pretty Alice* needs a mascot; and what
better mascot could she 'ave than Smut, I'd
like to know?

ALICE. [*Coming forward.*] How splendid! . . . Oh, Dick, do let him go! With such a mascot my namesake will surely sail to success!

DICK. [*Sadly divided in mind.*] If you, Miss Alice, and my good master, wish it, I can but say, "Yes" . . . And yet——

ALICE. It will only be for a time, Dick. Smut will come back safely enough, never fear!

CAPTAIN. Aye, aye, missy; that be true, I warrant ye! No ship could sink with a black cat on board! . . . An' sailors be superstitious folk, as well you know; they wouldn't let no 'arm come to their mascot! Why each and every man aboard will hold Smut's life above 'is own. And as for the luck—well, that 'll come sure enough; and when it does Smut's master won't be forgot— we 'll see to that! . . . Come, lad—time presses. What say ye?

[DICK *looks round helplessly at the eager faces about him, and mutely questions* ALICE.

ALICE. [*Pleadingly.*] Say "Yes," Dick! . . . Father would wish it, I know.

DICK. [*With an obvious effort.*] "Yes," then. . . . Take him, Captain, and be very good to him— he 's all I have in the world.

CAPTAIN. Trust me for that, lad!

[*They shake hands.*

KITTY. Oo, there now! . . . The little bit o' ribbon wot was all I 'ad to send in the ship 'll make 'im a lovely bow, that it will. Come to yer Auntie

Kitty, me darlin', and let 'er make yer beautiful!

> [*She ties the ribbon round* SMUT's *neck.*

CAPTAIN. All aboard, me hearties! Show a leg, show a leg! Ship the anchor! Lively does it!

> [DICK *hurriedly kisses* SMUT *as he is hustled out. All exeunt save* DICK, *who feels he cannot bear to see the last of* SMUT. *But* ALICE *turns back and watches* DICK *from the door.*

DICK. [*Sinking into a chair by the table and staring dejectedly before him.*] Well, anyhow, he'll be spared Arabella's tongue for a bit.

> [*The curtains close. . . . They reopen to show the curtain picture—*DICK, *his head on his arms, which are stretched across the table ;* ALICE *standing behind him, one hand on his shoulder.*

THE CURTAINS CLOSE

EMPEROR: A strange-looking beast! . . . Is it safe?

SCENE V (Full Stage)

In the Emperor's Tent on the Coast of Woozzoolloo

The Emperor *is seated on a dais.   On either side of this are* He Ho Hum *and* He Ho Ho, *his bodyguard. . . . In front of him, and to his right,* Captain Windlass *sits on a heap of gaudily coloured cushions, a wreath of flowers rakishly inclined over his left eye, and garlands hung about his neck in profuse array.*

Emperor. Wonderful! . . . Marvellous! . . . And again wonderful! . . . Even now I find it hard to believe. . . .

> [*He turns on his* Bodyguard *with sudden ferocity.*

If you have been lying to me, you miserable maggots——!

Ho and Hum. [*Both speaking together in a kind of chant.*] It is truth, O mighty one!

Hum. We!

Ho. Do!

Hum. Not!

Ho. Lie!

Hum. Hara!

Ho. Kara!

Hum. Hush!

Ho. Tush!

[*They simultaneously perform a quaint salute.*

Emperor. [*Raising his hand and speaking with great solemnity.*] Kasha! . . . Kasha! . . .

[*He then turns to* Captain Windlass.

Truly the great god "Poo Poo Tosh," to whom my people have burned incense for a thousand, thousand years without ceasing, must at last have heard our supplications and sent *thee* hither, O most Glorious! to bring us peace.

[Hum *and* Ho *chant as if performing a ritual.*

Hum. Golla!

Ho. Wolla!

Hum. Pom!

Ho. Pom!

Emperor. [*As before.*] Kasha! . . . Kasha! . . .

[*Continuing his speech.*

Little did I think when your ship sailed into the creek, that it was commanded by one who can speak our language. [*The* Emperor *and the* Captain *bow gravely to each other.*] Nor did I so much as dream that it carried the deliverer for whom we have looked so long—the mysterious animal—this—how do you name it?

Captain. Cat, Your Mightiness, C-A-T—cat.

Emperor. Ah, yes—Cat. . . . [*He resumes.*] This cat, who in a few short hours has rid my kingdom of the plague of rats under which it has groaned this many a year.

CAPTAIN. Yes, and 'e done it proper, Your Mightiness; what 'e didn't kill 'e chased into the sea!
You 've seen the last o' rats 'ere, and that I
promise you!   [HUM and Ho *chant as before.*

HUM. Chee!

Ho. Swish!

HUM. Chitty!

Ho. Bomb!

EMPEROR. [*As before.*] Kasha! . . . Kasha! . . .
As yet I have not seen this miracle-worker.

CAPTAIN. 'E 's just outside, Your Mightiness. I 'll
bring 'im in.

EMPEROR. Do so.

> [CAPTAIN WINDLASS *fetches* SMUT—*who also is
> garlanded—and places him in the middle of
> the tent, facing the* EMPEROR.

A strange-looking beast! . . . Is it safe?

CAPTAIN. Quite, Your Mightiness. . . . Come and
stroke 'is head!

> [*The* EMPEROR *descends, and places his hand
> upon* SMUT'S *head.* SMUT *mews; and his
> startled "Mightiness" retreats to the dais,
> where* Ho *and* HUM *cross their spears in
> front of him. He looks over this barrier
> apprehensively.*

EMPEROR. Is it angry?

CAPTAIN. Lor, no, Your Mightiness! 'E 's pleased,
that 's all! . . . Beg pretty for the gentleman,
Smut!   [SMUT *does so.*
There! . . .

[*The* EMPEROR *gingerly approaches once again, and ventures to touch* SMUT. . . *Nothing happens to alarm him this time, so he commences to speak as if issuing a kind of proclamation.*

EMPEROR. O most mighty hunter, deliverer of my country from devouring rats, happy indeed shall be thy future!   Here thou shalt dwell for ever! . . . I will build thee a mighty palace—and for every rat——

CAPTAIN. [*Springing to his feet.*] 'Ere, 'ere, 'old 'ard, Your Mightiness; Smut can't stop behind, you know!

EMPEROR. "Can't"!   I do not know the word. He will remain!

CAPTAIN. Impossible!

EMPEROR. To me nothing is "impossible"!   I will purchase the cat!

CAPTAIN. He is not mine to sell!

EMPEROR. Not yours—yet on board your ship? Explain!

CAPTAIN. Smut belongs to a poor lad in my master's employ—Dick Whittington by name—and Smut's all 'e 's got in the world, but 'e sent 'im to be our mascot on the voyage.   I promised Dick faithful as no 'arm should come to the cat, and pledged myself solemn, to bring 'im safe 'ome again.   And—'umbly beggin' Yer Mightiness's pardon—I 'm agoin' to keep that pledge and promise, come wot may!

EMPEROR. [*After looking stern, relaxes somewhat.*]
So. . . . There speaks an Englishman—and a
loyal friend!

> [*He shakes the* CAPTAIN *by the hand. And then
> continues musingly.*

A generous lad, too. . . .   [*He gazes at* SMUT.
His only possession. . . . His *all*.

> [*His mind made up, he speaks firmly.*

Never shall it be said that the Emperor Chungergunc knew not gratitude, and failed to recognize
generosity and loyalty! . . . This lad is poor,
you say?

CAPTAIN. Bitterly, Your Mightiness! But 'e would
not sell Smut, so you needn't think it!

EMPEROR. It shall not be expected of him! He
shall have his cat, and with it wealth beyond the
dreams of avarice! . . . On your way to the ship
my slaves shall lead you to my treasure caves.
From thence you shall take what gold, and
jewels, you can carry. Bear them to this lad
as the gift of the Emperor Chungergunc of
Woozzoolloo! . . . His fortune is made! . . .
I HAVE SPOKEN!

HUM AND HO. [*Salute and cry simultaneously.*]
Kasha! . . . Kasha! . . .

THE CURTAINS CLOSE

SCENE VI (Front Stage)

At the Fitzwarrens'

It is early morning. Enter ARABELLA, *obviously "put out."*

ARABELLA. Never was a sweet temper so tried as mine, I do declare! What a fate—to spend my days trying to wring their duty out of a pack o' lazy, good-for-nothing varmints——

    [*A sudden thought strikes her.*

Kitty! . . . KITTY!! . . .

Enter KITTY

KITTY. Yes, Cook.

ARABELLA. [*Mimicking her.*] "Yes, Cook," she says, as if butter wouldn't melt in 'er mouth! . . . I'll give you "Yes, Cook," in a minute! . . . Where's that worthless boy as ye're so set on?

KITTY. Dick ain't down yet, Cook—and I ain't——

ARABELLA. What, not down—at *this* hour! . . . Well, if that don't beat all! 'Oo does 'e think 'e is, I'd like to know? The feckless little lie-a-bed! . . . Go an' fetch 'im this instant!

    [KITTY *hesitates.*

Do you hear me? *This instant!!*

    [KITTY *runs.* . . . ARABELLA *again mimics her.*

"Dick ain't down yet, Cook!" . . . The idea!
Sakes alive, what's the world a-comin' to?

[*Exit* ARABELLA. . . . *After a short pause* KITTY
is heard calling in frightened screams,
"*Arabella! Arabella!*" *and she runs in,*
shaking and sobbing.

KITTY. Arabella! [ARABELLA *returns.*

ARABELLA. Now then—now then! Less noise there!
What's come to the girl? . . . If I hadn't the
temper of a heavenly saint I'd a-boxed yer
ears long ago, that I would. Stop yer snivelling,
do—an' speak up!

KITTY. [*Trembling.*] Oh, Cook. . . . [*Then with a
gulp.*] 'E's gone!

ARABELLA. Gone? . . . 'Oo's gone?

KITTY. Dick's gone!

ARABELLA. Dick?

KITTY. Yes, Dick! . . . Oh, Cook, 'is bed ain't
been slep' on, and 'e's nowheres to be seen.

ARABELLA. Nowheres to be seen? . . . [*Musingly.*]
What's 'is little game, I wonder. . . . Ever
since the cat went he's been grumbling about
the rats 'avin' come back——

KITTY. [*With a scream.*] Ow!—Mrs. Wagglechin—
yer don't think as the rats 'ave *ate him,* do yer?

ARABELLA. *Ate him?* . . . What, *bones* an' *clothes,*
an' *all*? . . . Talk sense, do, yer silly little
addlepate! . . . No, 'e's 'idin' under the straw,
I shouldn't wonder. . . . I'll just go an' look
for meself—an' if I catch 'im——

[ARABELLA *goes out, rolling up her sleeves.*
[ALICE *enters singing to herself. She stops
abruptly at seeing* KITTY *in tears.*

ALICE. Why, Kitty—what ails you?

KITTY. Oh, miss—it's Dick!

ALICE. Dick?

KITTY. Yes, miss. . . . Oh, miss, 'is bed ain't been
slep' on, and 'e can't be found no 'ow!

ALICE. But, Kitty, I don't understand.

KITTY. 'E's been mopy ever since we 'eard as the
ship 'ad gone down, an' grievin' something cruel
for Smut, an' Arabella 'ave always 'ad a grudge
against 'im, an' she's been worse than ever o'
late. . . . Oh, miss—I expect he's in the river,
that's it—that's where you'll find 'im—'e's in
the river!

[ARABELLA *returns, grumbling to herself.*

ARABELLA. Well, 'e ain't in the attic—that's
certain. Just wait till I catch 'im—I'll teach
'im to be funny, and play 'ide-an'-seek with me!

ALICE. What is this I hear, Cook? Is it true that
Dick cannot be found? Kitty, here, has been
saying dreadful things. . . . If aught amiss has
befallen Dick, my father will hold you responsible,
for he was in your charge.

ARABELLA. Sayin' dreadful things, 'as she! 'Old
me responsible, will 'e! . . . Me! *Me !* What's
poured out all the sweetness of my saintly nature
upon that poor motherless lad, to say nothin' of
'is darlin' cat! But I'll bear no more! . . .

The worm 'as turned! . . . After forty years o' faithful service, I 'll go — I gives a month's notice—a month's notice here and now, and I 'll go straight to the Halderman an' tell 'im so to 'is face—see if I don't!

[*Exit* ARABELLA *followed by* ALICE *and* KITTY.

THE CURTAINS OPEN

SCENE VII (Full Stage)

On the Northern Heights above London

Dick is discovered standing by the milestone gazing back at London. Unconsciously his right hand is pressing against the talisman.

DICK. Good - bye, London! . . . Good - bye, dreams! . . .

[*The* OLD WOMAN *enters.*

OLD WOMAN. Good morrow, Dick Whittington!

[DICK *turns with a start.*

DICK. You!

OLD WOMAN. Of course; you summoned me?

DICK. I? . . . Summoned you?

OLD WOMAN. Of a truth.

DICK. Good mother, you are mistaken; I did no such thing.

OLD WOMAN. Indeed, my son; and you did! . . . Did I not tell you at our last meeting to remember me when your ship came home? Well, your ship *has* come home, and you *have* remembered me, for just now your thoughts called me hither.

DICK. It is true that I was thinking of you. But it is not true that my ship has come home—that will never happen—it has gone to the bottom

—and Smut with it! . . . I have lost
everything. . . .

OLD WOMAN. Dick Whittington, the *Pretty Alice*
has *not* gone to the bottom! . . . Why did you
leave London, lad?

DICK. After Smut went I couldn't stand Arabella
any longer. . . . Then we heard the ship had
gone. . . . And all that I prize most seemed so
far beyond my reach——

OLD WOMAN. In other words, you lost faith, and
ran away from trouble. For shame, Dick! . . .
Do you remember my prophecy?

DICK. Yes—I have remembered it too often, for
'twas an idle saying.

OLD WOMAN. *It was Truth!* . . . And I am here
to complete that which could not be said until
your ship had come home. . . . Now mark me
well! All that you most prize is yours for the
asking, go now, and take it!

DICK. [*Impressed in spite of himself.*] Who are you,
good mother; and why do you come to me?

OLD WOMAN. Do you not know me?

DICK. No.

OLD WOMAN. Then for you I am nameless. . . .
I come at some time or another into each life of
every human soul: well for that soul if it know
me, and listen. . . . But I do not always appear
as I am now. Sometimes I am in the colours of
a sunset; sometimes in a flower. Sometimes I
look forth from the eyes of a child; sometimes I

am in the voice of the wind; sometimes in the roaring of the ocean; sometimes in the song of a bird. My guises are many, but to all I come, once, at least! . . . Dick Whittington; have Faith, have Courage, *go back!* . . . The Prize is yours—take it!

[*The bells are ringing softly.*

Hark to the bells! Once you could not hear their message. Listen well—for now your ears are open!

[Dick *stands listening to the bells with growing wonder. The* Old Woman *moves slowly away, turning once to look back at him, and raise her hand as if in blessing, ere she passes from sight.* . . . Dick's *lips move soundlessly as if forming words. Suddenly his eyes light up.*

Dick. Mother, they are saying: "Turn again." "Turn again. Turn again—Whittington!"

The Curtains Close

SCENE VIII (Front Stage)

A Street in London

The bells are ringing. . . . Dick *enters, running.*
He stops to listen.

Dick. Still the same message! . . . "Turn again,
Whittington," and then : "Lord Mayor of
London."

[*He repeats the latter phrase reflectively.*
Lord Mayor of London! . . . Yet it may not be
impossible. Alice once told me of a poor lad,
and he——

[*The bells have almost died away. . . .* Captain
Windlass *enters, trolling a song, and
shouts for joy at the sight of* Dick.

Captain. Dick! . . . Dick! . . . Well met, me
lad; well met, indeed! Come, come; don't look
at me like that! Do you take me for a ghost?

[*He takes* Dick *by the shoulders and shakes him.*
There! . . . Pretty vigorous for a ghost, eh?

Dick. [*Still rather dazed.*] But, but, they said the
Pretty Alice had gone down with all hands!

Captain. Stuff, laddy; stuff! . . . Why, we 've had
the greatest voyage in history!

Dick. [*Hesitating.*] And—and, Smut?

Captain. Smut, laddy, is the 'ero of the piece!

45

DICK. Then he's *not* dead?

CAPTAIN. *Dead*—not much! He's made a fortune for you. You're a rich man, Dick; thanks to Smut.

DICK. Thanks to Smut?

CAPTAIN. Thanks to Smut!

DICK. A fortune?

CAPTAIN. That's it—a fortune!

DICK. Then the Old Woman *was* right after all!

CAPTAIN. I don't know nothin' about any Old Woman, but what I'm tellin' you is gospel truth. Come with me to the master's, and I'll prove it! . . . Lively does it — don't stand mooning there!

DICK. That's it—take me to Smut. Where is he?

CAPTAIN. Hard a-port, laddie; and then, straight ahead!

       [*Exeunt* DICK *and* CAPTAIN WINDLASS.

SCENE IX (FULL STAGE)

The Kitchen at Alderman Fitzwarren's

ROSA, MARY, ARABELLA, KITTY, ALICE, *and* DICK
with his arm about SMUT, *are discovered listening
to* CAPTAIN WINDLASS, *who is evidently in the
midst of a narration. He is sitting on the table
among several baskets containing gems and gold
nuggets. One or two bulging sacks lie on the
floor at his feet.*

CAPTAIN. ——and then, after Smut had killed all
the rats, the old king wanted to buy 'im. . . .
But I told 'is Mightiness that 'e couldn't do that,
no 'ow. 'E wanted to know fer why. So I ups
and tells 'im all about Dick, and 'ow Smut was
all 'e 'ad, and 'ow 'e sent Smut along to be our
mascot to bring luck to 'is master's ship. . . .
That seemed to please the old boy, for 'e does a
bit of hard thinking, and then bursts out as 'ow
'e 'll make Dick the richest man in England. . . .
Next 'e sends me to 'is treasure caves with a
great escort, and they carries down enough gold
and jewels to sink the ship twice over. I stowed
away all I could get aboard—and 'ere we are!
  [*He slips off the table and points to the baskets
    and sacks.*

47

You 're a rich man now, Dick, and I 'm right glad—you deserve it!

ALICE. Oh, Dick—it 's splendid!

KITTY. Oh, Dick—it 's wonderful!

ARABELLA. Come to Arabella, me dear, wot 's loved you, and mothered you, ever since you come to London! . . . I always said as you were one in a thousand!

        [DICK *submits to the embrace.*

DICK. Thank you—thank you, all! . . . If I am rich I shall not forget you, never fear! And when I have a house of my own, Kitty shall be my head cook!

KITTY. Oo—Dick!

ARABELLA. [*Bridling.*] Now, then, now then! Don't go putting ideas into 'er 'ead—she 'll be getting uppish in a trice—and if she does——

CAPTAIN. Come, come, mistress, we mustn't 'ave no 'arsh words to-day! . . . An' now—to the master! It 's 'igh time I reported to 'im, but at the risk of 'is displeasure, I had to come to Dick first, seein' the circumstances. . . . Come along with me, lad; and then, when business is over, we 'll make merry, see if we don't!

THE CURTAINS CLOSE

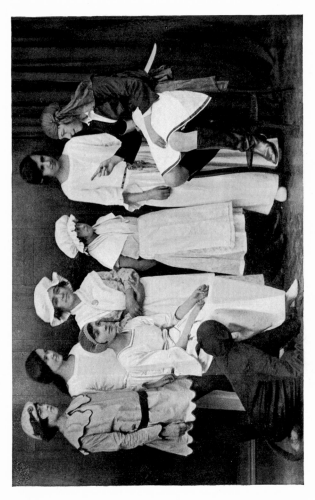

CAPTAIN WINDLASS: You 're a rich man now, Dick, and I 'm right glad—you deserve it!

SCENE X (FRONT STAGE)

An Ante-room at Alderman Fitzwarren's

*A pleasant uproar of junketing and merry-making in
full blast—music, shouts, and a babble of voices—
is heard behind the scenes. . . . A door slams
loudly, shutting out the riot, and* ALICE *appears
through the curtains. . . . Soon afterwards the
invisible door is opened again, and for a moment
the happy noise gushes forth once more. Then,
for the second time, the door is slammed, and*
DICK *appears. . . .*

DICK. Why have you left the merry-making?

ALICE. I wanted a little rest from the noise and
glare.

DICK. Will you do me a great favour?

ALICE. Willingly!

DICK. [*Taking the bean from about his neck.*] Then
wear this always. [*He holds it up.*] It is a
talisman of great power—it has brought me all
I ever dreamed of. Anon I will tell you how I
came by it.

[*He hands it to* ALICE.

ALICE. Thank you, Dick! . . . [*She takes the bean
from him, and after turning it this way and that,
puts the ribbon about her neck. . . . Next she
turns to* DICK, *and taking his hands impulsively*

E   49

in hers, exclaims.] Oh, Dick, I am so happy to think of your bright future!

DICK. Alice—don't! . . . [*He half turns away.*] I am so tired of the phrase—it has been used a hundred times in the past hour! *My* future—*my* future—*my* future—it sounds *lonesome* somehow, and I've had enough of lonesomeness! . . .

[*He turns back to her.*

Alice, may I speak my mind?

ALICE. Of course, Dick.

DICK. Then, instead of that cold phrase, won't you—won't you say—*our* future?

[ALICE *turns away.*

There—you are offended!

ALICE. No, Dick; not offended, but glad and proud! . . . Henceforth, as you wish it so, the future shall be—*our* future!

[*She extends her hand to* DICK, *who bends to kiss it. As he does so* SMUT *pops his head between the curtains and mews loudly. Both turn to him, laughing. Whereupon* SMUT *rises erect, and walks down to the front of the stage, where he speaks to the audience as follows.*

SMUT. And with these words our humble drama ends,

No more as actors we address you, friends.

We thank you for your company to-night,

We 've tried to give you pleasure and delight,

And hope you have enjoyed our simple play!

* And now, before you wend your homeward way,
We pray you join us in a joyful duty;
That ancient tribute: "Britain, Home, and
   Beauty."
Arise, my friends, with heart and voice to sing
Our song of loyalty—*God Save the King!* *

[*While* SMUT *has been speaking the Epilogue, the
Cast—excepting* CHRISTMAS *and* TIME—*have
been assembled behind the curtains, the* OLD
WOMAN *in the centre. . . . On* SMUT'S *final
words the curtains should be opened, and
every one take part in the singing. Next the
music changes to a cheerful march.* SMUT,
ALICE, *and* DICK *turn right-about-face. The
rest of the Cast—except the* OLD WOMAN—
exeunt L and R, and SMUT *places one arm
about* ALICE, *and the other about* DICK, *and
all three pass slowly up-stage. . . . As they
reach the* OLD WOMAN *she lifts up her
hands in benediction; and at this moment
the curtains should be closed.*

* * Where it is not desired to end the performance with the
singing of the National Anthem the lines between these points
may be omitted and the following spoken in their stead:

"And now, before you wend your homeward way,
   We tender you our wishes strong and true;
   God Bless You All, and All most Dear to You!
   And so we end with many a hearty cheer:
   Friends—may you prosper—this—and every year!"

The play should then be concluded as described above, except
that vigorous cheering takes the place of the singing.

ALI BABA

A PHANTASY IN PASTICHE

To
" BARBARA "

HER PLAY

THE PEOPLE

Barbara Rencroft.

Her Dream-self.

Robert Rencroft (*her brother*).

His Dream-self.

* Mrs. Rencroft (*their mother*).

Ali Baba (*a wood seller*).

Zieah (*his wife*).

Saadi (*his son*).

Selim (*his donkey*).

Ylil (*their little maid*).

Casim Baba (*brother to Ali*).

Naggiala (*his wife*).

Morgiana (*their slave*).

The Captain of the Forty Thieves.

First Robber.

Second Robber.

Baba Mustapha (*a cobbler*).

* The Genie of the Lamp.

* These characters should be played by adults: the Genie by the tallest and thinnest available.

THE SCENES

NOTE: The *outer* curtains should be used at the beginning, and again at the end of the play: drawn apart for Scene I, and closed at the conclusion of Scene XI. . . . Between these two points only the *inner* curtains should move.

SCENE I (FRONT STAGE)

The "Old Nursery," Witcholt Manor

*The parting of the curtains discloses two children,
BARBARA and ROBERT RENCROFT. They are
both dressed in white; BARBARA in a simple
frock, with white socks and shoes, ROBERT in a
sports shirt over which is pulled a white jumper,
white flannel trousers and white rubber-soled
shoes. . . . BARBARA is seated on an oblong
"humpty" large enough for two, absorbed in a
book. ROBERT stands, hands in pockets, obviously very "fed up."*

ROBERT.   You can say what you like, Babs, but
it's absolutely, completely, and altogether *feed-
ing*!   I didn't mind the measles—after all I only
had three and a half spots and a cold in the
head; it was different for you I admit, you looked
like nothing on earth outside the Zoo, old thing!
[*He grins, and then continues.*] But I can't stick
this beastly quarantine—not a soul near us for
days and weeks—might as well be dead! [*He
kicks at nothing and hunches his shoulders.*]
And as for that "hard court" of dad's—it's
just a wash-out!   When he laid it down, he

said: "There, tennis all the year round!" But
is there? Not much! . . . I did think I'd
get a slosh this afternoon. What happens?
Rain!

[*During all this* BARBARA *has apparently heard
nothing, nor has she moved, save to turn the
pages of her book. . . .* ROBERT *now seems
fully to realize her lack of attention. For a
second or two he glares at her unresponsive
back and then bursts out.*

Hang it all, Babs, you might listen to a fellow!
I've only got *you* to talk to—dad's carried off
Uncle George to the study—and all you can do
is to stick your nose in a rotten book! [*He
moves nearer.*] What is it, by the way?

[BARBARA, *seemingly lost to the world, slowly
turns a page. . . .* ROBERT *shouts.*

Babs! *What are you reading ! !* BABS! ! !

BABS. My name is Barbara. . . It's *not* a rotten
book. . . . I've never looked like anything in
the Zoo. . . . And oh, Bobby, how you do *talk !*
[*She resumes her reading.*

ROBERT. [*A little confused by her sudden animation.*]
Talk, do I? *Talk ! !* Well, what else is a chap
to do, I'd like to know? [*Suddenly a new
grievance seizes him.*] And I'll thank you not to
call me "Bobby." [*He repeats the word slowly
and with intense disgust.*] "Bobby!" Any-
body would think I was two—squirming in
"crawlers"—and dribbling!

BABS. [*Looking up, and speaking with studied reflectiveness.*] Yes—I expect you did dribble at that age.

ROBERT. [*Darting a furious look at her, and then replying with an air of aloofness.*] Well, anyhow, *you* did . . . very sloppy about the chops, *you* were.

BABS. [*Intensely calm.*] I suppose you think that's going to annoy me!

ROBERT. [*With gusto.*] I don't *think*—I *know*!

BABS. [*Thoughtfully.*] Yes—Lorna was quite right about you.

ROBERT. [*Positively jumping at the mention of "Lorna".*] Now don't drag that ginger-headed, green-eyed clothes-prop into this! She's nothing to do with it. . . . I don't want to hear what she said and I don't care, anyway! [*He swings suddenly round.*] What was it?

BABS. Never mind! . . . But she stuck a label on you, my child, the first time she saw you. And you needn't pretend you don't like her, because it won't wash! Whenever she comes to tea with *me, you* follow her round with your eyes out on stalks like an adoring pekinese and do anything she asks!

ROBERT. [*Hotly.*] I don't! [*Then changing his ground.*] Besides, one must be polite to visitors.

BABS. [*With crushing irony.*] Polite!

ROBERT. [*Determined to change the subject.*] I don't know what you mean by that, but *you* haven't

been polite enough to answer my question yet—
what are you reading?

BABS. *Ali Baba.*

ROBERT. [*Repeating the words incredulously.*] Ali
Baba! GOSH! ! [*And then, recovering from his
astonishment.*] You complete KID! ! !

BABS. [*Defensively.*] Why? It's a jolly good story.
Although [*her eyes grow dreamy*] I should like to
change it just a little bit. I'm sure it was
different really, you know—"Morgiana," and all
that—she wasn't quite an ordinary servant, she
simply must have been a princess or something—
and the robber chief—he couldn't have been just
a common thief—I expect he was an exiled
sultan, or——

ROBERT. [*Cutting in with a laugh.*] Or a sheik!
You've been going to the pictures—that's
what's wrong with you!

BABS. [*Not to be shaken from her train of thought.*]
No, I'm ever so serious, really. I'm sure it
wasn't all quite as tame as they make out. . . .
Do you think so?

ROBERT. [*With lofty good humour.*] Don't ask me!
It's such ages since I read the thing that I
can't remember much about it! . . . But I
seem to recollect something about cutting a chap
in four pieces, and then sewing him together
again, that wasn't too bad.

BABS. [*With a return to irony.*] Yes; that's just
the sort of bloodthirsty thing that would stick

in your mind—Lorna's quite right—boys are
like that. . . . She also says they "trample."

ROBERT. Oh, *does* she! . . . Oh, *do* they! . . . It's
just the sort of absolute bilge she would talk—
you're a little ass to listen to her. . . .
And it's like your cheek—this wanting to ginger
up the classics!

BABS. It isn't cheek—it's *imagination*.

ROBERT. Gosh! . . . Hark at the kid! . . . Where
does it get the long words from? . . . "Imagination"—I don't believe you know what it means!

BABS. [*Gently.*] Oh, yes, I do; because *I 've* got it,
and *you* haven't!

ROBERT. What!—Well of all the—— [*Suddenly
seeing daylight.*] Here, I know where that came
from—your precious green-eyed Lorna! I can
just hear her saying it! But let me tell you it's
all wrong; and your blessed superiority as well
. . . you girls talk as if you were different, as if
you weren't *real*, somehow, but you jolly well
are, and when it comes to business you're as
keen as keen. Why, in a swop you always do
better than I do——

    [*He breaks off as* MRS. RENCROFT *enters,
    calling out.*

MRS. R. Hello, children. . . . Bobby, darling, you
look very hot and bothered.

    [ROBERT *is "winded" by this address; and
    BABS, rising, and putting an arm around
    her mother, says:*

BABS. Darling, you mustn't call him "Bobby," it makes him dribble!

[ROBERT *gasps again.* MRS. RENCROFT *looks with a comprehending smile from one to the other.*

MRS. R. [*Contritely.*] Ever so sorry, old man. . . . It slipped out.

ROBERT. That's all right, Mumski! . . . But [*Reasonably.*] it is rather awful, isn't it?

MRS. R. [*Deeply serious, as befits the moment.*] Yes, Robert. Absolutely awful.

[*We are strongly aware of the mutual affection surrounding the group as they stand, the children each with an arm about their mother, all three smiling. . . . In her left hand* MRS. RENCROFT *holds a parcel, and as her arm is partly encircling* ROBERT'S *shoulder, this object catches his eye.*

ROBERT. Here—what's the mystery?

MRS. R. [*Holding the parcel aloft.*] Ah, what?

BABS. [*With a burst of intuition.*] I *know*! . . . It's the "Magic Mirror"!

MRS. R. Yes, that's just what it is—the "Magic Mirror." But how did you guess?

BABS. Oh, I don't know. . . . I just *knew*, that's all.

ROBERT. "Imagination"—eh, Babs?

BABS. Shut up, Bob!

MRS. R. Listen, children! . . . You remember Uncle George was expecting a professor from the

ROBERT: Hum—looks very harmless, doesn't it? . . . Not in the least "spooky."

British Museum to look at some of the things
he's brought back from Persia?

BABS AND BOB. Yes.

MRS. R. We have had a wire from the professor to
say he is coming this afternoon—two days before
we expected him—and Uncle George has taken the
car into Inglebury to meet the train. He said he
was quite sure the professor would want to take
the mirror back with him, so, as you had been
promised a peep into it, your uncle unpacked it
before he started—and here it is!

ROBERT. Good for uncle!

MRS. R. You may keep it for this afternoon. Take
great care of it. Uncle has told you all about it,
I hear.

BABS. Oh, yes; it's *wonderful*. . . . Ever so old.
. . . Uncle said it was old when Persia was the
Persia of the Arabian Nights.

> [MRS. RENCROFT *unwraps the mirror and they
> crowd together to examine it.*

ROBERT. Hum—looks very harmless, doesn't it?
Not in the least "spooky." And it's a wash-
out as a mirror. The middle isn't glass at all—
it's just a piece of metal—rather like dirty zinc.
It couldn't reflect anything!

BABS. But you silly—it's not supposed to *reflect*
things—it *shows* you things—you *see* things
in it.

ROBERT. Not in that, my child! It's much too
dirty.

Babs. Oh, mother! Isn't he dense sometimes?

Robert. Not so dense as your old mirror!

Mrs. R. [*Laughing.*] Now then, you two—no scrapping!

Babs. [*Who has been examining the mirror closely.*] There are some words here, round the edge. I wonder what they mean?

Mrs. R. Ah, I was curious about them, too. Uncle George said they really couldn't be rendered into English—our tongue wouldn't convey the exquisite subtlety of the Persian—but they mean something to this effect: "Vision is to the Childlike."

Babs. [*Murmuring the words to herself.*] "Vision is to the Childlike."

Mrs. R. And now, dears, I must fly! Be good. Uncle will come up as soon as he gets back.

> [Babs, *still looking into the mirror, crosses to the "humpty," and sits down.* Mrs. Rencroft *pauses just as she is leaving, calling* Bob *over to her.*

Bob! . . . [*She lowers her voice a little.*] Don't tease Babs too much. . . . She isn't quite strong again yet. Her measles were worse than yours, remember, so don't overdo it.

Robert. [*With an understanding grin.*] All right, Mumski. I won't forget! . . . She's no end of a decent kid really, but a chap must keep his end up, you know!

> [Mrs. Rencroft *departs laughing.* Robert

*looks after her for a moment before turning
slowly back into the room. . . .* BABS,
*still sitting on the "humpty," gazing into
the mirror, suddenly calls out with suppressed
excitement.*

BABS. Bob! . . . Bob! . . . There's something
moving in the mirror!

ROBERT. [*Inattentive.*] Go on!

BABS. But there *is*! It's like smoke. Quick,
come and look!

ROBERT. [*Strolling nonchalantly across and peering
over her shoulder.*] I don't see anything. . . .
[*Then with rising excitement.*] Yes, I do, though—
you're quite right—it *is* smoke!

BABS. Look; now there's a bright spot of light in
the middle.

ROBERT. Yes, I can see that too! . . . And it's
spreading—pushing the smoke away.
[*He sits beside her, and they stare into the
mirror, their heads very close together.*

BABS. It's quite clear now; and there's a courtyard—and two women. . . . One of them is
walking up and down, up and down, and
wringing her hands as if in trouble. Isn't it
weird, Bob?

ROBERT. Rather! . . . The middle of the mirror's
gone altogether. We seem to be looking right
through it. . . . By Jove, it's clearer than
ever! That woman looks as if she is calling
out.

F

Babs. Yes, I can see her lips moving. And Bob—
I can hear her voice—and some words too! . . .
Oh, Bob, listen! . . . Listen! . . .

Black Out

Under cover of the darkness the curtains are opened, and the children make a quick exit, taking with them the "humpty," the book, and the mirror (Mrs. Rencroft has already carried away the tissue paper in which the mirror was wrapped), while Zieah's voice, gradually growing louder, is heard crying, "Ay-ee. . . . Ay-ee. . . ."

SCENE II (Full Stage)

The Courtyard of Ali Baba's House.

*The curtains at the back are looped up to make an
arch-like entrance. . . . Zieah is walking to and
fro, evidently under stress of emotion. Ylil,
sitting upon the ground, is calmly sewing, a
shallow, circular basket by her side.*

Ylil. [*Looking up at the restless, moaning figure
before her, and speaking with intentionally soothing
accents.*] Pray you, dear mistress, calm yourself.
. . . Our good master is but delayed. . . .
Assuredly no harm has befallen him, for Allah
watches over the kindly.

Zieah. Ylil, be silent! Such idle chatter vexes
me. . . . 'Tis easy for thee to prate of peace;
what knowest thou of such afflictions as mine?
. . . Ay-ee. . . . Ay-ee. . . . That Fate should
trick me so cruelly! . . . My sister, married to
my husband's brother, waxes in fortune and
happiness, whilst I, united to this worthless Ali,
wane in poverty as a spent moon sinks into the
oblivion of the west! [*She resumes her walk,
crying at intervals, "Ay-ee. . . . Ay-ee. . . ."
Suddenly she halts before Ylil.*] And thou canst

call forth the protection of Allah for this good-for-nothing on the score that he is "kindly"! . . . Aye, "*kindly*" he is! . . . Yes, indeed, so "*kindly*" that he would steal his wife's food to feed a starving beggar, or neglect and desert her that he might tend a sick dog! . . . "*Kindly*" sayest thou—"*kindly*"——

YLIL. E'en though I displease thee, mistress, indeed thou doest him a wrong, for our good master Ali is as gentle as the sun at eventide.

ZIEAH. [*Turning upon her like a whirlwind.*] Speak but one more word in that strain, and, before Zantras, I will flay thee, and cast thy vile body——

>   [*A sound of singing is heard, and she breaks her tirade to listen. . . . YLIL, who has been cowering upon the ground, sits up. Her smiling face discloses that she recognizes the singer. She makes a tiny obeisance, and murmurs:*

YLIL. Allah is good.

>   [ZIEAH *hurries through the central entrance into the passage beyond the courtyard and gazes up the lane. She returns looking more distraught than ever.*

ZIEAH. [*With despairing calmness.*] It is even worse than I thought. Selim carries no wood, and both he and his master are dancing! Our purse is empty—in the house there is neither bite nor sup—and they have spent the hours carousing!

ALI: Get thee to thy stall, my Selim, ere long thy faithful services shall be amply rewarded.

[*She sinks to her knees, and, covering her face with her hands, rocks to and fro.* . . . Y<small>LIL</small>, *leaving her basket on the ground, crosses to the centre opening, which she reaches just as* A<small>LI</small> *and* S<small>ELIM</small> *enter.* . . . Z<small>IEAH</small> *has spoken nothing but the truth—they are indeed dancing!* A<small>LI</small> *breaks off to tap* Y<small>LIL</small> *playfully on the cheek.*

A<small>LI</small>. So, little melon-flower, thou art the first to welcome us! [*He presses money into her hand.*] Go—prepare supper. . . . Hist!—in thine ear—anon thou shalt wear a new gown! . . . Where is thy mistress?

[Y<small>LIL</small> *indicates the crouching* Z<small>IEAH</small> *and slips out, smiling happily.* . . . A<small>LI</small> *dances forward a step or two, the donkey following; he then strikes an attitude.*

O, my beloved Sunflower—my Silver Moon-daisy —dazzling as the Orb of Day—mysterious as the Star-spangled Mists of Twilight—Arise; shed upon me the light of thy countenance and rejoice! . . . The Hour has struck!* The Day has dawned!* The Future is ours!* All things are possible!* Allah is great!   [*He salaams reverently.*

[* *Here* S<small>ELIM</small> *performs little dances, but as* A<small>LI</small> *salaams he solemnly bows, and bends his knees.*

Z<small>IEAH</small>. [*Uncovering her face and speaking with biting sarcasm.*] Go, quickly, and plunge thee into the tank. . . . Perchance cold water will wash the wine-dregs from thy brain; and when thou art sobered mayhap some sanity may be restored thee.

ALI. [*Whose humour is too good to be damped even by this onslaught.*] What—thinkest thou I am drunk? Well, then, thou art right, for so I am; drunk, gloriously drunk! But not with wine— with Joy—with Success—with late-won Victory! . . . See; thou also shalt be drunk even as I, my Celestial Rosebud—I will infect thee too, and thou shalt dance and sing even as I! [*He snatches up* YLIL'S *basket, and plunging his hand into one of the sacks slung over* SELIM'S *back, pulls out a fistful of gold which he allows to trickle through his fingers into the basket which he holds out the while in front of the crouching* ZIEAH.] Gold, O Zieah! . . . Gold! . . . What may we not compass with so much gold to aid us?

[ZIEAH *starts to her feet, recoiling from the money with an expression of horror.*

ZIEAH. Ay-ee. . . . Ay-ee. . . . Woe! . . . Woe! . . . I see it all! . . . Poverty hath driven thee mad, and in thy madness thou hast turned bandit! . . . Take thine ill-gotten gains, take them! Who knows what blood may not be upon them? But thou shalt restore everything—make full amends—or I will inform against thee. Feckless I knew thee, but that thou shouldst sink to crime is beyond all! [*She turns away, raising her hands and letting them fall with a gesture of despair.*]

Ay-ee—for what past sin must I atone by
sheltering a murderer and a thief as husband?

[*During the earlier part of this outburst* SELIM's
*knees knock together, and he looks sadly
at* ALI.

ALI. [*His joyous humour no proof against this attack,
grows suddenly grave and speaks with gentle
reasonableness.*] Zieah; wife; these are hard
words! . . . But I perceive thou art distraught
—beside thyself—and as yet the truth is beyond
thy compassing. . . . Be seated. I can explain.
Do not judge me unheard!

[*Somewhat reassured by his quiet manner,* ZIEAH
sits. . . . ALI *turns to the donkey and
removes the bags of gold.*

ALI. Get thee to thy stall, my Selim; ere long thy
faithful services shall be amply rewarded.

[*After sundry skittish caperings* SELIM *trots
away. . . .* ALI *then approaches* ZIEAH.

Listen, O Keeper of the Seven Delights—it was
thus. . . . After the siesta, I, with Selim, left
thee to gather wood to sell to our worthy
neighbours. . . . How, I know not, but soon
we were upon a strange road, and anon found
ourselves in an unknown valley, standing before
a great rock. . . . Scarce had we reached this
spot, when the sound of an approaching cavalcade
smote upon our ears, borne down the ravine on
the far side. . . . Quickly we sought shelter in
the bushes hard by, just in time to hide from a

posse of forty men who cantered into the space
before the rock, and formed a semicircle with
their leader in the middle. I scanned them
closely, and I swear they were not from our
parts. By their unfamiliar dress and habit I
judged them to have come from beyond the desert.
As I looked, behold, the leader stepped up to
the rock-face and raising his hand, cried: "Open
Sesame!" and, as I live, with a noise of thunder,
the rock opened wide a great porch, and the
horsemen passed from sight within its gaping
jaws! Whereupon, the fissure closed of itself,
leaving no trace. In a moment all was as
before. . . . Had I dreamed? No! . . . Upon
the ground lay the packs, arms, and other
chattels laid aside by those within. I dared make
no move, knowing not when the band would
re-emerge, and shortly, lo! the rock reopened,
and, pausing only long enough to collect belongings, the cavalcade disappeared the way it had
come. . . .

ZIEAH. Strange, indeed!

ALI. Aye; but prepare for greater marvels! . . .
I waited till all sound of the march had died away.
Then, stepping before the rock, *I* raised *my* hand,
and cried, even as the chief had cried: "Open
Sesame!" At my words the rock opened, and
greatly daring I passed through the portal! . . .
How shall I describe what then burst upon my
gaze? Gold, jewels, bales of merchandise, sacks

of coin, riches and wealth of every description,
and in such profusion that the mind reeled before
so vast a spectacle!

ZIEAH. But what meant this? . . . Whence came
these things?

ALI. 'Twas clear that I had stumbled upon the
storehouse of a band of robbers. . . . For years
unnumbered must such loot have been hidden
in that wondrous cave! And now, think, beloved; this long-hid secret is mine! To win
wealth beyond our wildest dreams I have but
to make two more journeys to the cave. What
I shall then remove, great to us, will make no
perceptible inroad into that enormous store.
. . . Rejoice with me, O Zieah! Poverty is over!
The future smiles! Our son shall sit with the
great ones, and wed the highest in the land!

> [ALI *raises* ZIEAH *gently to her feet, as* ROBERT
> *and* BARBARA *enter, stepping forward
> quickly. They look just as they did when
> we saw them last, but in reality they are in
> their dream-bodies.*

ROBERT. [*Excitedly.*] I say; jolly fine, Ali, old man!
. . . Congratulations and all that.

BABS. [*Pulling him back by the coat and speaking
in an agitated whisper.*] Come back, Bob, what
are you doing! Goodness knows what may
happen if they see us!

> [*But* ALI *and* ZIEAH *have seen and heard
> nothing.*

ALI. More of this anon. . . . We must be discreet,
and waste no time. . . . These bags must be
buried at once.

[*He stoops to pick them up.* ZIEAH *interposes.*

ZIEAH. Hast counted the money?

ALI. Nay.

ZIEAH. 'Twere well to know how much we bury.

ALI. But to count it, coin by coin! 'Twould take
a moon!

ZIEAH. I will borrow a measure from Naggiala, wife
to Casim: with that it can be done quickly.

ALI. Well thought! . . . Go on the instant, and
return speedily.

[*The curtains are closed, leaving* BABS *and* BOB
on the front stage.

SCENE III (Front Stage)

A Passage-way near the House of Casim

ROBERT. I say, isn't it all queer and exciting?
Did you notice they couldn't see us?

BABS. Yes; and they couldn't hear us either, thank
goodness! Bob, it's a bit awful—supposing one
of them *did* see us. . . . I think I'm a bit
scared!

ROBERT. Oh, no, you're not! . . . Whatever else
you may be, you're no funk! . . . Besides, if
there's any trouble you can always stand
behind me. . . . Hush—somebody's coming.

[*They draw back as* NAGGIALA *enters. She is
half-way across the stage when she sees
CASIM coming, and halts. He enters, whereupon she bursts forth wrathfully.*

NAGGIALA. So thou hast deceived me again, thou
black-hearted seed of a poison apple!

[*He makes as if to speak, but she rushes on.*
How many times hast thou told me that we are
a thousand times richer than thy brother Ali and
his wife?

CASIM. 'Tis true! . . . Ali is naught but a husk-fed
beggar!

NAGGIALA. "Husk-fed beggar," forsooth! I tell

75

thee thou liest! Mark me—thy brother cannot *count* his gold—he needs must *measure* it!

CASIM. That Ali cannot *count* his gold is just—*he hath none to count!* . . . Get thee within and rest. The sun hath addled thy brains!

NAGGIALA. Nay; jibes cannot shake me, for this time I have the truth. Behold!

[*She places something in his hand. He turns it over in his palm and exclaims.*]

CASIM. A good gold piece. . . . Whence came it?

NAGGIALA. From the house of Ali!

CASIM. Ha! . . . A good story—but—sun-born!

NAGGIALA. Thinkest thou so? Give me thine ear. . . . A little time agone Ylil came running to beg the loan of a measure. I could not credit that in that scanty household could be aught in quantity enough to measure; therefore, before parting with it, I smeared a little tallow beneath the measure's base. Anon it was returned, and upon the tallow was that golden coin! What sayest thou to that?

CASIM. Can it be that that two-faced scorpion has been laughing at us in his sleeve? And I thinking I could twist him round my finger! . . . But I *can*—I swear it! . . . There is some mystery here; thou didst well to warn me. . . . Get thee within and hold thy peace. . . . I will to this brother of mine, and by Zantras, the secret of this hoard of gold shall be mine before dawn!

[*He rushes out. . . . NAGGIALA returns to the house nodding and smiling.*

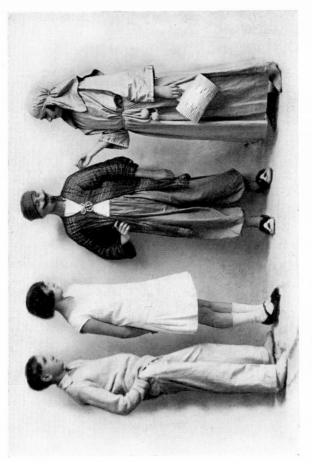

NAGGIALA: Nay, jibes cannot shake me, for this time I have the truth.   Behold!

ROBERT. Poor old Ali! He's going through it!
. . . What happens next, I wonder?

BABS. Don't you remember?

> [*He shakes his head.*

Why, Casim worms the story from Ali, goes to
the cave, gets in and can't get out again because
he forgets the word of command, and then——

> [*The curtains slowly begin to part.*

Look out, something is happening!

> [*After a little hesitation they separate, one to
> each side of the proscenium.*

SCENE IV (FULL STAGE)

Near the Cave

The curtains should be arranged to form a plain background for this scene, and Scene VI.

CASIM *enters. . . . He is excited and nervous and looks about him eagerly.*

CASIM. There is the single pepper-tree. . . . There is the scrub where Ali hid. . . There is the second road. . . . No doubt about it—yonder is the Rock of the Cave! . . . What have I to say? . . . "Open Sesame!" . . . Yes; that's it! . . . Strange how difficult I find it to remember those simple words, they have nearly escaped me a dozen times in the past hour. . . . "Open Sesame!" . . . Yes—I have them now! [*He looks intently round.*] No sign of life. . . . Ali's Forty Thieves are far afield to-day—the farther the better for my purpose!

> [*He laughs . . . and then, after a last hurried glance round he makes off toward the cave. . . . A few moments later we hear his cry: "Open Sesame!" A thunderous roll follows the words, repeated after a couple of seconds, it indicates that the rock has closed after him.*]

. . . There is a short pause after the second roll has died away, before two of the robber band enter. One, raising his hand to his mouth, gives a long, soft call: "Oo-eee!" and in response the CAPTAIN *and others of the band make their appearance.*

CAPTAIN. Where is he now?

FIRST R. Within the cave, master.

CAPTAIN. You have seen him close—do you know aught of him?

[*Both* ROBBERS *shake their heads.*

FIRST R. Nay, master; nor can we hazard even a guess from whence he may have come.

CAPTAIN. Go, quickly, reconnoitre and report!

[*Exit* SECOND ROBBER *towards the cave.*

'Tis a mystery how he hath fathomed our secret. For seven centuries has our cave remained inviolate, known only to our band. And now, at this very moment it is being desecrated! . . . We must act, and that without more delay.

[*The* SECOND ROBBER *returns.*

Well?

SECOND R. I can hear him within. It would seem that he hath forgot the words of power, and is trying at random to recover them. . . . He is nigh to madness with terror!

CAPTAIN. Poor fool! . . . Go you to the cave. Cry it open. . . . The moment the rock rolls apart the man will rush forth. Slay him at once—cut his carcass into four pieces, and hang them within the cave. . . . If he hath confided his knowledge to others, and they follow him, the body will serve as a warning. . . . Obey!

[*Exeunt all except the* CAPTAIN. *He stands with his back to the audience, watching and listening.* . . . ROBERT *pokes his head out, calling across to* BARBARA.

ROBERT. Babs, did you hear? I knew that cutting-up business came in somewhere! [*Commences to come out.*] I 've a good mind to go and have a look!

BABS. [*Looking out on her side and waving him back.*] Don't be so utterly beastly! And do keep back—they 'll see you!

ROBERT. They can't; we 've proved that.

[*From without comes a voice crying* "*Open Sesame !*" *followed by the thunderous roll of the opening rock. Then a long-drawn scream.* . . . *Then — silence.* . . . BABS *withdraws with a half-smothered gasp.* . . . ROBERT *stands his ground.*

ROBERT. I say; they 've done it! ! Some yell that, what?

BABS. [*Poking her head out again.*] It 's all perfectly horrid! How can you stand there pretending to enjoy it!

[*They both draw back.* . . . *From without comes the voice crying* "*Shut Sesame !*" *followed by the thunderous roll, as before.* . . . *After a slight pause the* ROBBERS *return.*

First R. It is done, O master! The dog will trouble us no more.

Captain. 'Tis well! . . . The poor rash fool hath paid the price of his folly! . . . And now; away! . . . This business hath delayed us too long. 'Twill be a hard ride if we are to reach Zabe by daylight.

> [*They go out hurriedly, and the sound of their galloping horses dies gradually into the distance.*

Robert. [*Emerging again.*] Well, that's that! . . . Now what I want to know is—how do we get away? . . . To begin with, I don't remember how we got here.

Babs. [*Who has come out to join him.*] Look, Bob; isn't that Ali and the Donkey coming?

Robert. My word, yes! . . . I say he's going to get a nasty shock when he goes into the cave!

Babs. Let's warn him, or something.

Robert. You forget; he can't see or hear us. . . . I don't think there is anything we *can* do.

> [Ali *and* Selim *enter by the auditorium and mount to the stage by a gang-plank.*

Ali. Aha, my faithful Selim; a few more steps— and we are *there*! [Selim *suddenly stops.* . . . Ali *prods him.*] Come, come, thou art stopping too soon! [*But* Selim *refuses to budge.*] What ails thee? . . . 'Tis not like thee to be so stubborn. . . . To the cave, quickly! [Selim *shakes his head.*] Haste thee! . . . Haste thee! ! [Ali *pushes*

G

from the rear, but Selim *stands firm. . . .* Ali *desists and, walking round, stares at* Selim *with a puzzled expression.*] Thou art like a stranger. . . . I do not know thee in this mood. . . . Dost thou not want to go into the cave ? [Selim *shakes his head again.*] Why not ? [Selim *is very restive.*] If I do go alone, wilt thou wait here, and not run away ? [Selim *nods.*] Very well. See that you abide my coming. [Ali *goes out. . . . *Selim *exhibits acute discomfort and is almost grovelling upon the ground when we hear, after *Ali's *call of "Open, Sesame !" the thunderous roll of the opening rock.*

Black Out. Curtains Close

SCENE V (FRONT STAGE)

A Room at Casim's

ROBERT *and* BARBARA *are discovered looking about them.*

ROBERT. Where are we now? . . . I suppose Ali did find Casim? It all disappeared before we really knew.

BABS. Oh, yes, he must have. . . . Look, this is Morgiana coming, I'm sure!

    [MORGIANA *enters, looks carefully round, and then calls softly to someone without.*

MORGIANA. Come!

ALI *enters.*

We shall be alone here, and can continue our talk.

ALI. Dost think thou hast this strange story clear?

MORGIANA. Aye. . . . [*She marks each point on the finger of her left hand.*] How the cave was found. . . . How my master, Casim, forced the knowledge from thee. . . . And how, on thy second visit, Casim's body hung within.

ALI. Thou art a marvel of comprehensions! . . . Now use thy wits yet more. . . . It must be given out that Casim died naturally. How is this to be accomplished?

MORGIANA. All could be done easily were only his body not dismembered.

ALI. Can no way be found to fasten it together?

MORGIANA. I can think of none as yet. . . . The body is on the donkey?

ALI. Aye.

MORGIANA. Is there aught else?

ALI. Nothing! . . . Selim could carry no more.

[*Suddenly he remembers.*

Oh! . . . But so as not to come away quite empty-handed, I snatched up this old lamp as I passed out!

[*He draws it from his waist-band.*

MORGIANA. [*Taking it from him, and turning it about.*] 'Tis greatly tarnished!

[*She rubs it with her sleeve, there is a momentary "black-out," and the* GENIE *stands between them. . . . On seeing him* ALI *starts forward crying.*

ALI. Where didst thou spring from, thou eaves-dropping dog? I will twist thy neck for thee!

[*The* GENIE *points a finger at* ALI, *and he is stricken motionless.*

GENIE. [*To* MORGIANA.] I am the Genie of the Lamp. What are your commands?

MORGIANA. [*Dazed.*] What sayest thou?

GENIE. In thine hand thou holdest the Lamp of Aladdin. Ask, and I obey!

GENIE: I am the Genie of the Lamp. What are your commands?

MORGIANA. [*To* ALI; *having a little recovered her wits*.] If we had Baba Mustapha here he could sew the body together!

[ALI *nods—with a wary eye on the* GENIE.

MORGIANA. [*To the* GENIE.] Slave, fetch hither Baba Mustapha, the cobbler!

[*A momentary "black-out," and* BABA MUS-TAPHA *is in the room—flustered, and out of breath. . . . The* GENIE *and the* CHIL-DREN *have vanished.*

BABA. [*Opening his eyes*.] Where am I? . . . What is this? . . . A moment ago I sat sewing at my stall, and now I am—I know not where! . . . Ay-ee; I am too old for these sudden flights!

MORGIANA. Pardon us our haste, good cobbler, but the need is urgent. . . . Wouldst earn much gold?

BABA. Yea. . . . If it be the fruit of honest toil.

MORGIANA. Then follow apace. We have a very special task for thee. . . . Come!

[*They go out: and the curtains part.*

SCENE VI (Full Stage)

Near the Cave

The Captain *and the* Second Robber *are discovered. From without comes the voice of the*
First Robber *crying "Shut Sesame!" followed
by the sound of the closing rock. . . . A
moment later he rushes in.*

First R. The body is gone, master! There is no
trace of it within the cave!

Captain. Then the intruder *had* confided in others!
. . . Who knows how many now share the secret
of our cave? . . . We must lose no time in
tracing them—if they exist. . . . Give heed: we
three, disguised, will make our separate ways to
the city, and there pursue inquiries. . . . To-
morrow, at this hour, we will meet here, and
report. [*They salute and part.*

The Curtains Close

SCENE VII (Front Stage)

A Passage near the Home of Ali Baba

Enter Morgiana *and* Saadi.

Saadi. If only we could win consent to a betrothal between us!

Morgiana. 'Tis more than ever impossible, Saadi, since thy father hath become so rich. . . . Remember, I am but a slave.

Saadi. Nay, nay; 'tis *I* who am the slave! . . . *Thy* slave!

Morgiana. A pretty speech, and I thank thee for it! . . . But we must be practical. The course of true love never runneth smoothly, but true love can accomplish miracles. . . . Let us be patient!

Saadi. Patient, say you! . . . Oh, Morgiana, patience is so easy to preach, and so hard to practise!

[*They go out; and the curtains part.*

SCENE VIII (FULL STAGE)

The Courtyard of Ali Baba's House

*For a moment the stage is empty. . . . Then, very
cautiously, SELIM peeps in at the central
entrance. . . . Finding the yard deserted, he
enters, and peers about. . . .*
YLIL *enters, and starts at seeing him.*

YLIL. Selim, you bad donkey, you know you are
forbidden to come here unattended! [SELIM
waves his head towards the entrance, but YLIL
doesn't catch his drift.] Go at once, or I will
fetch Morgiana to thee! [*At the mention of*
MORGIANA *he is very excited and nods.*] What;
art thou not afraid of Morgiana? [*He shakes his
head.*] Well, we shall see! . . . [*She goes to the
side and calls.*] Morgiana! Morgiana!

MORGIANA *enters.*

See, Morgiana; what hast thou to say to naughty
Selim?
MORGIANA. Why, Selim, what art thou doing here?
[SELIM *jumps about and then looks over to the
entrance several times.*] What, dost thou want
me to follow thee? [SELIM *nods vigorously.*]

88

Now, at once? [SELIM *is even more emphatic.*]
Go, then, and lead the way!

[SELIM *trots out, followed by* MORGIANA *and*
YLIL. . . . ROBERT *and* BARBARA *enter
from the side.*

BABS. That darling donkey is absolutely sweet! A
perfect *lamb*!

ROBERT. Why do girls always mix their thingumies
when they gush over animals? . . . How on earth
can a *donkey* be a *lamb*? You'll be calling the
poor thing a *duck* next!

BABS. Well, so he is! . . . And *you* think so too,
really!

ROBERT. [*With a chuckle.*] Oh, well; perhaps I
do. . . . He certainly is a knut!

BABS. [*Ironically.*] Oh, no, he couldn't be! You
are mixing your whatsisnames now! If he isn't
a *lamb*, he can't be a *knut*; you might just as
well call him a *grape-fruit*!

ROBERT. [*Sighing wearily.*] Oh, law! how you
girls do argue! Of course he's a knut! It's
quite different really. . . . Now do chuck it, and
listen; here comes Ali with his missis.

[ALI *and* ZIEAH *enter from the side, as* MORGIANA
returns through the central opening.

MORGIANA. Master; mistress; I have some doubtful
news for thee. Selim did reveal it to me. . . .
He trotted in, and by signs gave me to understand that he wished me to follow him. . . .
That did I, and passing without, perceived upon

the outer door a large cross drawn with chalk.
. . . Looking about me quickly, lo, a man shield-
ing his face with his robe slunk away down the
alley by the weaver's shop.

ZIEAH. What meaning hangs to this, think you?

ALI. Can it be that I have been tracked by the
Robbers?

MORGIANA. Time alone will show. . . . I saw I
could not remove the cross without leaving
traces behind, so I chalked a cross upon each
of the neighbouring doors, and this will
surely confuse any one who would trace our
dwelling.

ALI. 'Twas well done! . . . In truth thou art a
treasure, Morgiana!

MORGIANA. I am glad to have pleased thee,
master! . . . Now will I watch the coming of
those who marked the house. Rest assured we
will circumvent them should their intentions be
evil.

[*She goes out. . . . The children, who have
been standing at the side, have now withdrawn
from view.*

ALI. A faithful child! . . . We did well to take
her in when Naggiala came here after Casim's
burial. . . . When our wealth is firmly estab-
lished I will free her.

ZIEAH. I should be happier if she did not find such
favour in the eyes of our son. . . . I have other
plans for Saadi.

ALI. We will go into that later. . . . But let us
not make too free with what is another's. . . .
Saadi's future is Saadi's. And love, if it be
true love, is as beautiful as the scent of flowers
in the cool of the evening. . . .

THE CURTAINS CLOSE

SCENE IX (FRONT STAGE)

Outside the Workshop of Baba Mustapha

It is early morning. . . . (The lighting should be dim, and pink tinted.)

BABA MUSTAPHA *comes out slowly, and looks about him.*

BABA. How beautiful is the morning before it is stained with the turmoil of daily life! . . . Hail to thee, fair Spirit of the Day-spring! Every morn thou bring'st a draught of Youth's Eternal Elixir to vivify this age-worn earth! . . . I am old; and my earthly eyes and ears grow dim: but with the Eyes of the Soul I clearer see thy Glory, and with the Ears of the Spirit I hear thy Voice of Flame!

    [He salaams; and returns within to fetch a little stool, and the tools of his trade. . . . This done, he sits and commences to sew a sandal. . . . At length the CAPTAIN *enters, and stands watching him.*

CAPTAIN. In truth, my father, thou must be deep enamoured of thy work to rise thus early to practise it!

BABA. My son, my work is my earthly duty. . . .

BABA MUSTAPHA: Not so, not so, my son! I am no Sage. Call me rather a *Seeker* who, by the blessing of Allah, hath made some findings.

I have trained my body to perform it of itself
that my mind may be free to gaze upon *Reality*.

CAPTAIN. *Reality* is a thing that I have long sought,
but alas, try as I will, I cannot recognize its
face. . . . Tell me, O my father, what see'st
thou when thou lookest upon *Reality*?

BABA. I see *That* that *Sleeps* in the *Rocks*. *Breathes*
in the *Flowers*. *Stirs* in the *Brutes*. And *Awakens*
in *Man*. . . .

CAPTAIN. [*Softly.*] So! . . . I perceive thou art
true Sage, as well as Cobbler.

BABA. Not so, not so, my son! I am no Sage. . . .
Call me rather a *Seeker*, who, by the blessing of
Allah, hath made some findings.

CAPTAIN. I fain would talk more of these wonders
with thee—but I am upon a quest and dare not
tarry. . . . Mayhap thou canst help me! Know'st
thou of any man in this city, once poor, and now,
on a sudden, become rich?

BABA. Nay, my son, I have heard of none such.

[*The* CAPTAIN, *turning away with a gesture of
disappointment, strolls up and down in
thought. . . . Then he stands, again watching* BABA *at his sewing.*

CAPTAIN. In truth thou art a master of the craft!
I marvel that thou canst see to sew, for the
light is not yet strong.

BABA. There is light enough for such rough work.
Why, not long since I sewed a man's body
together in dimmer light than this!

CAPTAIN. [*His eyes flashing.*] A strange task! For
whom didst thou perform it? And where?

BABA. I cannot tell! . . . Magic hung about it.

CAPTAIN. Speak more of this, I pray you!

BABA. [*Putting down his work.*] The story is soon
told. . . . In the late of the afternoon I was
within at work upon a delicately embroidered
slipper, when, lo, in the twinkling of an eye, I
found myself transported, by some unknown
means, to a chamber wherein were a man and
a woman, strangers to me. . . . When I had a
little recovered from the rapidity of my transit,
the woman offered me much gold if I would use
my skill upon some special sewing. . . . I con-
sented, and was led to a chamber wherein lay the
body of a man, neatly cut into four pieces. . . .
These, by request, I joined together. . . . This
done, the woman blindfolded me, and led me
forth. . . . Anon, when the bandage was re-
moved, I found myself standing by the Great
Mosque. . . .

CAPTAIN. [*With intense eagerness.*] Listen closely;
much hangs to this! If thou wilt come with me
to the Great Mosque, and from thence, blindfolded, canst retrace thy steps to the house where
thou didst the cobbling, I will double the sum
that the woman gave thee for thy services. . . .
What sayest thou?

BABA. 'Tis a generous offer! . . . But I much
doubt me whether I can find the way. . . .

[*He considers the matter, as he slowly gathers
up his belongings. . . . At length he turns
to the* CAPTAIN.

Come within—we will talk more of this.

[*They go out; and the curtains open.*

SCENE X (Full Stage)

The Courtyard of Ali Baba's House

ROBERT *and* BARBARA *are standing by the central opening.*

ROBERT. Ali seems to have forgotten Aladdin's Lamp. He doesn't know when he's well off. . . . Just fancy getting hold of a thing like that and then to make no use of it! My hat, I wish *I* could have it for ten minutes!

BABS. But the poor old thing has had a rather worrying time, hasn't he?

ROBERT. Well, that's rather what I mean. . . . He could clear up his worries with the Lamp.

[ALI *enters—thinking deeply.*

ALI. [*Musing.*] The thought of that cross upon the gate hangs over my mind like a dark cloud——

ROBERT. [*To* BABS.] There you are! Why doesn't he call in that Genie?

ALI. [*Continuing his reflections.*] It is a portent of evil. Would I could fathom it!

[*He stands wrapt in thought.*

ROBERT. Look here; I'm going to *make* him hear sense! [*He steps forward.*

BABS. Oh, Bob, do be careful.

96

ROBERT. [*Confidently.*] That's all right, watch me!
[*He speaks from behind* ALI, *and almost into his
ear.*] I say, Ali, old man, why don't you make use
of the Lamp? [*But* ALI *hears nothing, so* ROBERT
repeats more slowly.] Why don't you use the Lamp?
[*Still* ALI *is unmoved. . . . One can see* ROBERT
*bracing himself for a pronounced effort. He
speaks with forceful intensity.*] The Lamp! . . .
The LAMP!

> [*This time* ALI *does hear something. . . . He
> starts and cries out.*

ALI. Who spoke?

> [*At his cry* BARBARA *drags* ROBERT *back. He
> puts an arm about his sister, standing
> protectively between her and* ALI, *who
> swings suddenly round as if he expected
> to surprise someone in the rear, crying out
> again.*

Who spoke?

> [*It is plain that he cannot see the children, and
> he exhibits astonishment at finding himself,
> as he thinks, alone.*

ALI. [*Still looking about him.*] By Zantras, I swear
I heard a voice! . . . Ho, there! [*He strides
to the opening and looks out, left and right;
afterwards turning back into the yard.*] No one!
. . . Who, then, cried: "The Lamp!"? [*The
significance of the words begins to dawn upon
him—and he grows suddenly solemn.*] 'Twas sure
the Voice of Allah, [*He salaams.*] for the reminder

H

comes in the nick of time! . . . [*He hurries to the side, calling.*] Morgiana! . . . Morgiana! . . .

Morgiana *enters.*

Morgiana—the Lamp of Aladdin?—thou hast it safely?

MORGIANA. Aye, master!

ALI. Fetch it, instantly!

[MORGIANA *obeys. . . .* ALI *takes the Lamp from her.*

Stand apart!

[*They separate, and he rubs the Lamp. . . . A momentary "black-out," and the* GENIE *stands between them. . . .* ROBERT *and* BARBARA *have withdrawn from view.*

GENIE. What are thy commands, O my master?

ALI. What means the chalk mark upon my door?

GENIE. 'Twas made by one of the Robber Band who traced thee hither; Morgiana's trick hath baffled him, but know that their Captain hath found thee through Baba Mustapha.

ALI. What is his purpose?

GENIE. Disguised as an oil merchant he will beg thy hospitality, but his oil jars will contain no oil. . . . In each will be hidden a Robber who at a given signal will spring forth to slay. . . . Thus do they hope to regain possession of the Cave.

MORGIANA. How shall we act?

GENIE. [*To* MORGIANA.] This captain — Coggia

Hassan by name—is brother to the Sultan of the Tribes of the Desert, and lives in banishment. The sultan is dead, without issue, and Coggia will reign in his stead. . . . This shall be revealed by restoring to him certain documents which I will procure. . . . [*To* ALI.] Trust me, O master, and all will be well! . . .

ALI. I will trust thee, Genie.

GENIE. Ali Baba, thou art known to the *Mighty Ones* as "Kind Heart," therefore I venture to petition thee.

ALI. Speak, I will listen.

GENIE. Once I was a powerful spirit, but I fell; and was condemned as punishment to serve, for an eon of eons, whosoever should own the Lamp; unless I could find one kind enough to set me free. . . . Master, if when this evening closes thou art well content, release, I beg thee, a tired spirit who surely hath atoned his lapse!

[*The* GENIE *kneels.*

ALI. Rest assured it shall be as you wish. . . . But what must I do?

GENIE. Hand to me the Lamp.

[*The* GENIE *rises.*

ALI. If that is all, why didst thou not seize the Lamp for thyself when it lay in the Cave?

GENIE. Of my own accord I may not touch it. It must be surrendered to me freely by the owner.

ALI. Then to-night it shall be thine, I promise thee!

[*The* GENIE, *sălaaming, vanishes in a "black-
out." After which a hubbub is heard
without.*

ALI. [*Crossing to* MORGIANA.] This must be the
supposed merchant and his followers.   Go within,
and prepare refreshment.

[*Exit* MORGIANA. . . . *The noise without dies
down, and the* CAPTAIN *appears in the
entrance.*

CAPTAIN. Peace be upon this house!

ALI. And upon thee also!

CAPTAIN. Art thou the master here?

ALI. Even so! . . . What wouldst thou?

CAPTAIN. I am journeying to the First City of the
Desert with a freight of oil.   The day draws in,
and we must seek lodging for the night. . . . I
crave thy hospitality.   Wilt thou house us till
morning?

ALI. Assuredly. . . . The jars of oil, and thy small
retinue, can remain in the outer yard, and as for
thee, a tiny guest-room awaits thy patronage.

CAPTAIN. I am indeed thy debtor!

The CAPTAIN *enters.*

ALI. [*Calling.*] Saadi!

SAADI *enters.*

See the men without, and their jars of oil, well
bestowed.   [*Exit* SAADI.

CAPTAIN. This sanctuary is welcome, I assure thee!

I am fatigued, for I am not accustomed to ride upon a mule. When I travel, 'tis usually in a litter.

ALI. Thou art indeed fortunate! When I travel 'tis usually in a cloud of dust! . . . [*He claps his hands and cries.*] Zieah! Ylil! Naggiala! Bring hither a divan, our guest would be seated!

[*The three women carry out a small divan. . . . SAADI returns. . . . ALI waves the CAPTAIN towards the seat, saying:*

ALI. Rest, I pray you.

[*When both are seated he continues.*

Some refreshment is being prepared and will be ready anon. In the meantime thou shalt see my slave Morgiana dance, she is skilled in the art. . . . Saadi, summon Morgiana!

[*SAADI goes out. . . . He returns with a tom-tom, sits cross-legged, and strikes up a lively rhythm. . . . MORGIANA enters. . . . She is about to begin her dance when the CAPTAIN starts to his feet and, seizing her by the hand, stares at her arm, crying:*

CAPTAIN. Who art thou that bearest a birthmark shaped like a palm tree upon thine arm? I believed none beside my daughter to be marked thus—but she is dead. . . . Tell me who thou art.

MORGIANA. Good sir, I know not. . . . My master, Ali Baba, found me, a deserted child, upon a tiny oasis in the desert. He, and my kind mistress

Zieah, tended me until I was old enough to serve. Then Casim bought me as a slave. When Casim died I returned here. . . . I can tell thee no more!

CAPTAIN. Thou hast told me enough! . . . When my brother, the Sultan of the Tribes of the Desert, banished me, he took my daughter from me, as he said, to slay her, but behold, she stands before me!

[*A momentary "black-out," and the* GENIE *is between them holding out a scroll.*

GENIE. Read!

[*The* CAPTAIN *takes the paper, reads a sentence or two, and then cries out in astonishment.*

CAPTAIN. A second marvel! . . . This document is all I need to establish my claim to the kingship of of my country!

GENIE. [*Slowly, and with great solemnity.*] Coggia Hassan, thy brother is dead. Thy people await your coming.

CAPTAIN. [*Impressed and wondering.*] Who art thou?

GENIE. One who speaks from knowledge. . . . Attend!

[*He hands the* CAPTAIN *another, and smaller scroll, which the* CAPTAIN *reads with breathless interest.*

CAPTAIN. [*Looking up.*] Then 'tis all true! . . . [*He turns to* ALI.] Ali Baba, I will be frank with thee! Knowing that thou hadst discovered the Cave, I came here to kill thee. . . . And now I

find thou art the preserver of my only daughter.
. . . There is much to be said between us, but
let us here and now swear a pact. Return
with me to my country; share with me the
knowledge of the Cave; and to bring our
families the closer, my daughter, and thy son,
shall be betrothed!

[*Before* ALI *can speak the* GENIE *stops him.*

GENIE. Art thou satisfied, O my master?

ALI. Never more so in all my life!

GENIE. Remember, then, thy promise!

ALI. I remember, and fulfil it!

[*He draws the Lamp from his waistband and
gives it to the* GENIE.

GENIE. Master, I thank thee! . . . Now I am free!
. . . I go; and with thee, Naggiala, and little
Ylil, I leave the Joy of Service; with thee, Ali
and Zieah, the Joy of Kindliness; with thee,
Morgiana and Saadi, the Joy of Love; and with
thee, Coggia Hassan, the Joy of Kingship!

[*He lifts the Lamp above his head.*

Farewell! [*He rubs the Lamp.*

Farewell!

[*There is a "black-out," and when the light
returns he has vanished . . . and* ROBERT
and BARBARA *are standing right in front
of the stage.*

BABS. [*Excitedly.*] Oh, Bob, isn't it all lovely! You
see I was right! She *is* a princess! And he *is*
a sultan! And it's all ending happily!

[*But this time the children have been seen. . . .*
ROBERT *observes this first, and shouts.*

ROBERT. Look out, Babs! They've seen us!
They're coming for us!

[*There are cries of* "*Look, strangers!*" "*Who
are they?*" "*Intruders!*" "*Seize them!*"
"*Let them not escape!*"—*and a* "*black-out.*"
Thunder commences with the "*black-out,*"
and should continue until the light returns.

SCENE XI (FRONT STAGE)

The "Old Nursery," Witcholt Manor

When the light returns ROBERT *and* BARBARA *are sitting on the "humpty" gazing into the mirror, just as we left them at the end of the first scene. . . .* ROBERT *starts to his feet.*

ROBERT. [*Shouting.*] Look out, Babs! They've seen us! They're coming for us!

BABS. Bob! . . . Bob! . . .

    [*The thunder ceases—they realize where they are, and look at each other grinning.*

ROBERT. [*Drawing a long breath.*] Phew! . . . That quite took me in! I really thought it was *real*!

BABS. But it must have been real—in a way.

MRS. RENCROFT *enters.*

MRS. R. Well, darlings, did you hear the thunder?

ROBERT. Rather; but was it real?

MRS. R. Whatever do you mean, Bob? Of course it was real!

BABS. Well, you see, we thought it was in the mirror.

MRS. R. In the mirror! Babs dear, now *you* are talking nonsense! How could thunder be in the mirror?

BABS. Mummy dear, *anything* could be in *that* mirror! We've had a *wonderful* time with it! . . . First there was smoke—Bob saw it, too—and then a picture—and then we were right *in* it! . . . There was Ali Baba——

ROBERT. And Mrs. Ali.

BABS. And Casim——

ROBERT. And Mrs. Casim.

BABS. And a *lamb* of a donkey——

ROBERT. Oh, rather—and they sliced Casim up——

BABS. And Morgiana was a Princess, and the Chief Robber was a Sultan, and Ali had Aladdin's Lamp, and he let the Genie go——

ROBERT. And we were walking about in the middle of it, and they couldn't see us—except at the end, when they all pointed at us, and——

MRS. R. [*Laughing.*] And you—*woke up!*

BABS AND BOB. Oh, mother!

BABS. No, mother, really! . . . It wasn't an ordinary dream because we both saw the same. That never happens in an ordinary dream, does it?

ROBERT. No! . . . And besides——

[*The tea bell is heard to ring.*

MRS. R. Well, that's tea; so tell me all about it another time! Off you go—and wash your hands!

BABS. All right, mummy! . . . But it *wasn't* a dream!

ROBERT. No.

Mrs. R. No, dears, of course it wasn't—if you say so! . . . Now do hurry!

[*The children scamper away, and* Mrs. Rencroft *is left laughing.*

Mrs. R. Ali Baba—and Aladdin's Lamp—and Princesses—and Sultans—and Donkeys—and Genies! . . . And both dreaming the same! . . . What children they are! . . . All in the Magic Mirror, too. . . . [*She picks it up from the "humpty," and repeats in a tone of mock awe.*] The Magic Mirror! . . . [*She laughs again.*] Now let *me* see! . . . [*She gazes steadily into the mirror—then shakes her head and gives a little shrug.*] Nothing! . . . Of course not! How foolish one is! [*She raises the mirror to scrutinize the writing upon it.*] "Vision is to the Childlike." [*She shakes her head a little ruefully and repeats, stressing the last word a little.*] "Vision is to the Childlike." [*Quickly she glances in the direction that the children have gone.*] Ah!—so perhaps— after all. [*Then with resolute matter-of-factness.*] Oh, but what *nonsense*! . . . [*All of a sudden she is less confident.*] And yet—who knows—who really knows? . . .

[*And so we leave her—still questioning.*

COUNTY COUNCIL OF STIRLING
COUNTY LIBRARY
EDUCATION COMMITTEE

MADE AT THE
TEMPLE PRESS
LETCHWORTH
GREAT BRITAIN

STIRLING DISTRICT LIBRARY